A Land So Wild

by Elyssa Warkentin

ISBN 978-1-948272-13-1

Published 2018 by Carnation Books

CarnationBooks.com

contact@carnationbooks.com

San Jose, CA, USA

Contents

Chapter One: January – June 1850 7

Chapter Two: June – August 1850 31

Chapter Three: September – October 1850 65

Chapter Four: October – December 1850 94

Chapter Five: January – April 1851 129

Chapter Six: May – August 1851 159

Chapter Seven: August – October 1851 189

Chapter Eight: October – December 1851 219

Chapter Nine: December 1851 – August 1852 255

Chapter Ten: September – December 1852 295

Epilogue: 2014 319

Author's Note and Acknowledgements 321

About Carnation Books 325

Ah, for just one time I would take the Northwest Passage
To find the hand of Franklin reaching for the Beaufort Sea;
Tracing one warm line through a land so wild and savage!
And make a Northwest Passage to the sea.

– Stan Rogers, 1981

Chapter One:
January – June 1850

Sung by Imaruittuq at Igloolik during the darkness of the year of the second incursion; learned from Aippaq, who learned it from Ugalik, the first singer, five summers ago.

Aya, I think I have heard
(He has heard from the wind)
I think I have heard
(He thinks he has heard)
The sound of wood out in the wild.
Aya, Aya, Aya.

I think I have heard
(He thinks he has heard from the sea)
I believe that I hear
(He believes that he hears)
The sound of wood from the sea.

Aya, Aya, Aya.
Aya, Aya, Aya.

Here comes the wood from the sea.

Aya, Aya, Aya.
Aya, Aya, Aya.

✲ ✲ ✲ ✲ ✲

The Evening News
6 January 1850
P. 8

CAULDERSON EXPEDITION DECLARED LOST

Well will our readers remember with what joy and excitement we bid *bon voyage* to the Caulderson Expedition five long years ago, upon the expectation of at last discovering a Northwest Passage through the Arctic waters of America and through to the Atlantic Ocean. Captain William Caulderson professed the utmost confidence in his mission, his crew, and his ship, the HMS *Vanguard*. Reports of the *Vanguard*'s transatlantic crossing via the southern route and its resupply stop in Halifax Harbour in the spring of 1846 gave interested observers cause for similar optimism. However, once the ship entered the icy Arctic waters of Baffin Bay, it was spotted briefly by two hardy whaling vessels and was then lost to civilization. No trace of it has been found, despite frequent sweeps of the bay by those same whalers. And so, it cannot be unexpected that the Admiralty has today made the following announcement: *With grave sorrow, we announce that the HMS* Vanguard *has been classified as LOST by the Admiralty. It is not possible, in our estimation, that the ship or any of the men aboard her could have survived so long in such extreme conditions without making any successful attempt to contact civilization. We pray for the souls of the brave men lost.*

The elusive and deadly Northwest Passage has now claimed the lives of more than 200 good men. The Admiralty, however, remains firm in its belief that the Passage can be discovered, and will be discovered by British explorers.

✲ ✲ ✲ ✲ ✲

7 January 1850

TO: Sir Francis Hall
Ashfield Manor
Caterham on the Hill, Surrey

Sir Francis,

No doubt you have seen the Lord High Admiral's recent announcement regarding the fate of the Caulderson Expedition. To speak plainly, sir, I believe the announcement to have been preliminary. There are many within the admiralty who hold out hope, still, for Caulderson and who believe that his recovery is essential to her Majesty's imperial mission. I suspect you may share this opinion, given your extensive trade interests in the East. We have discussed this before – imagine the convenience to yourself, should a new trade route be discovered. In short, our interest in the recovery of the expedition is considerable.

I have always entertained the most sanguine views with regard to the discovery of ships. Notwithstanding five years have elapsed since tidings were received, yet I see no reason to despair. The grounds on which it appears to me reasonable that Caulderson and his men on the *Vanguard* should not be considered dead, but living, are these:

First. Because no evidence has been discovered of any catastrophe having befallen them. Neither the bodies of men, nor parts of ships, timbers, spars, stores of any description have been found, either afloat in the currents or washed up upon the shores. The captains of the whaling ships, men the most experienced in these matters, concur in asserting that it is next to impossible that a ship could be crushed and destroyed without any of their crews escaping and without some traces of the disaster being found.

Secondly. It is widely assumed that Caulderson would have sought the passage north on Parry's Sound and through Banks Straight into a vast sea of impenetrable floe ice, in which his recovery would be a hopeless mission. My cartographical analyses suggest otherwise. It requires but a transient glance at the Polar chart to see that between Baring Island and Prince Albert Land, only blank space is laid down. That quarter of the Arctic Sea, where it is most probable that the missing parties would be found living, or their fate ascertained, has never yet been mapped. What discoveries Caulderson may have made in this space he has not returned to tell; no one has yet followed him there.

Thirdly. The most experienced of Arctic explorers has consolingly assured us that life may be maintained in the farthest Arctic lands under circumstances that are at first sight seemingly the most hopeless; nature accommodates herself, and the hardships and sufferings of the first years would be mitigated afterwards. I think we may agree that where the sturdy Esquimeaux can live, there also can Englishmen.

Fourthly. At the utmost limits of northern travel attained by man, hordes of animals of various kinds (including ruminating animals) have been observed travelling still further north. Birds, of which almost incredible numbers are occasionally seen, take their flight northward, and the highest waters yet attained are frequented by the whale, the walrus, and the seal, which furnish not only food, but fuel and clothing. Surely your son can confirm this: he is, I understand, a superb naturalist.

Despite the above four points, the Lord High Admiral refuses to mount any sort of rescue operation. He is – forgive me, but he is set in his ways, and unwilling to consider opinions that differ from his own. As far as he is concerned, Caulderson is dead and the *Vanguard* lost.

Sir, I cannot agree with him, and I cannot abandon our men to a terrible fate on the ice when there is any possibility of saving them. I have, along with a group of four or five like-minded men placed high in the admiralty, resolved to quietly mount a rescue mission. It will have to be most discreet, of course: an entirely private venture. We do not wish to draw public attention to the attempt, and we will not run it through any Admiralty channels. We need to find a ship, and good men, and outfitters – and we must do it quickly. We have each pledged a considerable amount of money to the endeavor, but we require another two or three thousand to make a proper go of it. Even more than the money, however, we require a public face for this venture, for we cannot appear to be in public disagreement with the Lord High Admiral.

We would like you to front this mission, sir. Think of the time and money involved as a business investment: should Caulderson be found – should he have discovered the Passage! – what riches and what honour shall be yours! With what ease shall you conduct your Eastern trades! A small effort now will reap substantial benefits.

Think on it, sir, but not for too long. Our best chance for success lies now in speed.

Yours etc,

Vice Admiral Joseph Baring
British Navy
London Office

✲ ✲ ✲ ✲ ✲

8 January 1850

TO: Vice Admiral Joseph Baring
British Navy
London Office

Vice Admiral,

Well, well, Joe. What a tremendously interesting proposal you have put to me. You know I never could resist ship talk! Of course you understand I cannot promise such a large monetary outlay without significantly more detail as to the mission parameters – not even for an old Winchester chum. I shall need to know the names of all the backers, and of course you may rest assured of my discretion in the matter.

Come down to dinner tomorrow and we shall discuss it at length – I don't stand upon ceremony. Do you still dislike the train so much? I'll send my carriage.

Francis

⁂ ⁂ ⁂ ⁂ ⁂

TELEGRAPHIC MESSAGE: Sir Francis Hall to Vice Admiral Joseph Baring (9 January 1850)

YES ALRIGHT STOP I HAVE CONSIDERED THE POTENTIAL DIFFICULTIES OF YOUR LITTLE ENDEAVOR AND DO NOT FIND THEM TO BE INSURMOUNTABLE STOP YOU MAY RELY UPON ME STOP

⁂ ⁂ ⁂ ⁂ ⁂

10 January 1850

TO: Sir Francis Hall
Ashfield Manor
Caterham on the Hill, Surrey

Sir –

I was gratified to receive your telegram. With your assistance, I believe our undertaking stands every chance of success. Remember, only, that as far as anyone must ever know, the expedition is being mounted by you alone. The admiralty has no hand in it; you are merely indulging a somewhat eccentric enthusiasm for Arctic exploration. My career, and those of our other backers, is at stake.

Forgive my haste, but time is now of the essence.

We must immediately procure a vessel for modification and outfitting. Travel in Arctic regions is both arduous and unpredictable.

The ship must certainly be underway by June to take best advantage of weather and ice conditions in the passage.

I know of a sweet little vessel currently under construction by Scotts of Greenock on the Firth of Clyde and running 322 tonnes. She would suit us admirably. The expense is not small, but fits within the budget we set.

If we want her, we must act quickly; the admiralty is looking to acquire her itself.

Joe

PS. She's called the *Serapis.*

✲ ✲ ✲ ✲ ✲

BILL OF SALE

DATE: 11 January 1850
Sir Francis Hall of Surrey
Agrees to the purchase of the ship *Serapis*
Provided it is seaworthy and of good quality
From William M. Rice, Master Shipwright, Scotts of Greenock
At the price of £7,803
Upon the understanding that construction shall be complete by 1st May at the latest.

✲ ✲ ✲ ✲ ✲

TELEGRAPHIC MESSAGE: Sir Francis Hall to Embleton Hall (1 February 1850)

FOR GODS SAKE MASTER YOURSELF STOP RUMOURS ALARMING STOP WILL CALL AT YOUR ROOMS 3:00 TOMORROW STOP

TELEGRAPHIC MESSAGE: Embleton Hall to Sir Francis Hall (1 February 1850)

WILL BE OUT STOP

TELEGRAPHIC MESSAGE: Sir Francis Hall to Embleton Hall (25 February 1850)

EMBLETON PLEASE THINK OF YOUR FAMILY STOP THIS CANNOT CONTINUE STOP IT WILL BE FINISHED YOUR WAY OR MINE

* * * * *

27 April 1850

TO: Sir Francis Hall
Ashfield Manor
Caterham on the Hill, Surrey

Dear Sir,

Herewith your final progress report on the requested modifications to the *Serapis*, in order to prepare her for Arctic service. Ship extensively strengthened with timber (teak, English oak, Canadian elm) and 5⁄16 inch steel plating. Ten pairs of iron diagonal riders are set in the hold, with ten pairs of diagonal plates on the sides of the vessel between decks. To stand under snow and ice loads, the upper decks are doubled with 3-inch fir planking. Preston's Patent Ventilating Illuminators were installed to improve light and ventilation. Sylvester's Warming Apparatus is capable of warming the entire ship, installed with good results.

All work is now complete, and a list of expenses enclosed. We trust this is to your satisfaction.

R.&H. Green
Blackwall Yard
London Docks

* * * * *

29 April 1850

TO: Sir Francis Hall
Owner, *The Serapis*
London Docks

Dear Sir,

I hope you will forgive my impudence in writing. I am an acquaintance of Rob Green in the Blackwall Yard, and have been following his work on your ship with interest. I am no expert, but the modifications made to the Serapis are surely in preparation for Arctic service, are they not? And yet, I have heard of no planned expeditions. As it happens, I am sailor in want of a ship, and an Arctic voyage would suit me well.

When you begin manning and outfitting, please remember my name.

Sincerely,

David Maxwell
23 Little Eastcheap Street
London

* * * * *

30 April 1850

TO: Vice Admiral Joseph Baring
British Navy
London Office

Sir,

You should know that knowledge of our little venture begins to circulate – as we knew it must, before long. I had a letter from a Mr. David Maxwell, sailor, who wishes to enlist in an Arctic expedition and requests that I remember his name.

Certainly, it is time to assemble a crew. Despite my lengthy association with several members of the admiralty – yourself not least among them – I know little of the day-to-day workings of a ship; it would be best to find a captain and charge him with manning his own expedition. The public will accept my role as interested patron, but never would anyone who knows me believe me to have the expertise to outfit a ship.

Perhaps you or another of our backers can suggest some names? For obvious reasons, I should prefer not to advertise.

Sincerely,

Sir Francis

⁂

2 May 1852

TO: Sir Francis Hall
Ashfield Manor
Caterham on the Hill, Surrey

Sir Francis,

Good Lord! How extraordinary that David Maxwell himself should write to you. You would not know the man, but he was one of the finest lieutenants in the Royal Navy for a good many years. His temper ran a bit hot, perhaps, but he was well-enough liked, and better respected. Exemplary service record, too. Made quite a name for himself in the Baltic campaign, and then more recently in the West Indies. He served aboard the *Camperdown*, I believe it was, until Caulderton was given command of the *Plover* and requested Maxwell for his first mate. Of course, you remember the terrible business in Guadeloupe. Lost a good deal of cargo in the blaze, yourself, did you not? In any case, he was cited for bravery, but he has not been to sea since, and the Navy has completely lost sight of him.

Listen, why not meet him? He is – or was – a superlative seaman, and could be just the man we're looking for. It is extremely convenient that he has no current ties to the admiralty, and his personal connexion to Caulderton would surely only spur him on in his mission.

Please do keep me informed.

Joseph

* * * * *

TELEGRAPHIC MESSAGE: Sir Francis Hall to David Maxwell (3 May 1850)

LETTER RECEIVED STOP PLEASE JOIN ME FOR DINNER TOMORROW EVENING STOP I MAY HAVE A PROPOSAL FOR YOU STOP MY COACH SHALL COLLECT YOU AT 6:00 STOP BRING YOUR WIFE IF YOU HAVE ONE STOP

✲ ✲ ✲ ✲ ✲

5 May 1850

TO: Sir Francis Hall
Ashfield Manor
Caterham on the Hill, Surrey

Dear Sir Francis,

You cannot imagine with what surprise I received your letter this morning. To begin, I wish to thank you for your kind hospitality yesterday evening. I apologize that my wife was not able to join us, but as I explained she is in Sheffield on business related to her committee work.

Sir, are you in earnest with the offer you make me? I am an Acting Lieutenant, and have never held command. Your terms are very generous, and a one-year Arctic voyage is exactly what I seek. If you are indeed in earnest, I humbly and gratefully accept. I shall sign on by contract whenever you like. Thank you for your faith in me, sir. You shall not regret it.

Sincerely,

Mr. David Maxwell
23 Little Eastcheap Street
London

✲ ✲ ✲ ✲ ✲

9 May 1850

TO: Mr. David Maxwell
23 Little Eastcheap Street
London

Husband –

I will not mince words: your letter alarms me. I regret that I am not in London to discuss this matter in person, but as you know it was not possible to avoid the Sheffield assembly.

We have never been conventional in the observance of our marriage vows, and I will not stoop to ugly hypocrisy to argue my case. We agreed four years ago when we married that we should both reserve perfect freedom and independence even within the embrace of the other. Thus far, you have my blessing. And yet, David, think what you leave behind – of what you throw over! And to do it *for him*! Whatever you may tell yourself, whatever you may pretend, you must know that you do it for him. You will not wish to hear this, but please remember: the coward ran from you, Husband. He ran from what you offered. This is madness. This is suicide. I beg you to think of your health. And perhaps too, think of the situation in which you leave me. I do not wish to be alone in this world.

I know nothing of this Sir Francis Hall. Certainly, he is unconnected from the admiralty – and that, in itself, is further cause for alarm. Who is he? What does he know of you, to offer you command? I have grave misgivings, as should you.

I remain ever,

Your loving

Addie
Bath Hotel
66 Victoria Street
Sheffield, England

* * * * *

11 May 1850

TO: Sir Francis Hall
Ashfield Manor
Caterham on the Hill, Surrey

Dear Sir,

I agree, of course, that time is of the essence if we are to make the most of the brief Arctic sailing season. The usual southern crossing is far safer given the prevailing westerlies, but if we are to make the attempt this year (which is, we agree, of vital importance), sailing round the Azores will cost us too much time. I suggest the northern route. We'll have to beat into the wind pretty much the whole way, as well as into the waves, passing to the west of the British Isles, heading for a position approximately lat. 55°N., long . 30°W., then heading W.S.W for the American coast. It is unusual, but it has been done; I have spoken to men who have done it and I do not fear the risk.

Thank you for the extensive maps and charts you had delivered. I have studied them well, and agree that we should begin our search by passing between Baring Island and Prince Albert Land into the as-yet-unnamed strait which you have so carefully marked. Such, indeed, shall be my plan.

I have begun selecting my crew, as agreed. The perilous nature of the service and the secrecy which attends it, to say nothing of its philanthropic character, has made recruitment somewhat difficult. It is well that the ship is small, and we do not require a large complement of men. As you shall see, I have forgone a large contingent of officers in favour of a small crew of efficient and able men. A Mr. Lew Taylor has agreed to serve as my first mate. I have been intermittently acquainted with him for several years, as his service has allowed, and know him to be a steady, competent, and highly experienced sailor in Arctic waters; indeed, he has become a good friend, and I have no doubt that we will get on well together. It is my belief that his Arctic experience will counterbalance my own lack in that area. Of equal importance, he has managed to acquire extensive knowledge of several of the dialects spoken by the Esquimeaux people native to the Arctic, which will be of invaluable assistance as we seek news of the *Vanguard*.

Mr. Taylor has recruited a number of men to serve under us, all men he knows and has served with before. The preliminary roster is enclosed here. I have engaged Paul Carruthers to serve as ship's surgeon; although he's not seen active service for almost a decade, his disposition is of a cheerful and friendly nature such will greatly benefit the crew. Of the 30 or so berths aboard, almost all have now been filled.

I trust all meets with your approval.

David Maxwell
23 Little Eastcheap Street
London

⋄ ⋄ ⋄ ⋄ ⋄

11 May 1850

TO: Mrs. Maxwell
Bath Hotel
66 Victoria Street
Sheffield, England

My darling –

Do not be angry. Or rather, be as angry as you wish, but do not blame me, for there is no other way forward for me. You have witnessed my misery these past five years. I cannot bear to spend another year in this way – haunting the docks like a shade, useless and desperate. I have accepted the command of the *Serapis*.

You are mistaken when you ascribe my motives to anything but the concern of a lieutenant for the best commander he has ever known. If there is any good in me – he planted it. He made me into the man I am. I must do right by him, or try to.

I shall never leave you alone in this world, Addie. You must never fear that. The voyage is dangerous, I grant, but it is far from suicide. Our patron Sir Francis is certainly somewhat unusual in his dealings, but eccentricity is no crime. Once we are at sea, his strange influence will recede with the English shoreline.

I miss you and eagerly await your return. I will be there to meet your train.

Yours ever,

David

⁂

TELEGRAPHIC MESSAGE: Sir Francis Hall to Embleton Hall (12 May 1850)

HAVE PROCURED A BERTH ON AN OUTGOING VESSEL STOP YOU WILL REPORT FOR SERVICE AS SHIP NATURALIST STOP 12 MONTHS OF ARCTIC SERVICE STOP ITS THAT OR THE ASYLUM AGAIN STOP

TELEGRAPHIC MESSAGE: Embleton Hall to Sir Francis Hall (12 May 1850)

I CHOOSE THE ASYLUM STOP

TELEGRAPHIC MESSAGE: Sir Francis Hall to Embleton Hall (12 May 1850)

BE REASONABLE STOP 12 MONTHS TO REGAIN YOUR HEALTH AND CATALOGUE SAMPLES ARCTIC FAUNA AND FLORA STOP YOU WERE A SUPERB NATURALIST ONCE STOP I HAVE NO WISH TO IMPRISON YOU SON STOP

TELEGRAPHIC MESSAGE: Embleton Hall to Sir Francis Hall (12 May 1850)

I CHOOSE THE ASYLUM STOP

TELEGRAPHIC MESSAGE: Sir Francis Hall to Embleton Hall (12 May 1850)

SO BE IT STOP

✲ ✲ ✲ ✲ ✲

13 May 1850

TO: Miss Hannah Crawley
54 Oxford Street
London

My dearest Hannah,

How lovely it was to see you this afternoon and to spend even a scant half hour in your company in Hyde Park. The sight of your dear face, of your little lips curled in a smile, of the rose blooming on your soft cheek, is enough to give a fellow life. I know how difficult it is for you to escape from *his* watchful eye, and I am mindful of the risk you run. I would not presume to ask it of you were I not quite so desperately in love with you.

And yet, I cannot blame him. His paternal love protects that which I so love myself, and I will ever thank him for the care with which he guards my precious Hannah, though he never deign to look on me again.

I am a poor fellow, Hannah, and I know it. I am as unworthy as your father believes me to be. I thank God that I have somehow won your heart, and I trust in His wisdom that in time, your father will see his way to blessing our union.

Twelve months, my love. Twelve months of separation, of heartache, of loneliness – and then! You shall be mine, and no one – not your father, not anyone! – will be able to separate us ever again. We shall have our own little cottage, then, Hannah, and I will accept only the briefest of commissions, for I shall never wish to be away from your side. You shall have your own household, and your books, and a garden, and fat babies to adore, and I shall have you.

Wait for me. Be faithful. I will come.

Ever yours,

Lew

⁂ ⁂ ⁂ ⁂ ⁂

14 May 1850

PROVISIONING ORDER
Messrs. Gamble

On request of Sir Francis Hall, full provisioning of *Serapis:* thirty-one men for a twelvemonth's journey. Provisions to include adequate stocks of salt pork and beef, flour, sugar, lime, cheese, biscuit, butter, beer, pease, oatmeal, spirits, &c to secure full rations for the duration, plus another month for safety's sake. Further, full sets of clothing for Arctic conditions. Sir Francis requests that no expense be spared. Expected departure: 8 June. Timeliness is of the utmost importance.

* * * * *

TELEGRAPHIC MESSAGE: Sir Francis Hall to Embleton Hall (27 May 1850)

THANK YOU FOR SEEING ME STOP INTERVIEW MOST SATISFACTORY STOP SHIP SERAPIS STOP CAPTAIN D MAXWELL STOP REPORT 7 JUNE BY MIDNIGHT STOP

TELEGRAPHIC MESSAGE: Sir Francis Hall to Embleton Hall (27 May 1850)

GODSPEED SON STOP

* * * * *

27 May, 1859

TO: David Maxwell
23 Little Eastcheap Street
London

Captain Maxwell,

I am reluctant, always, to overstep your authority as captain of the *Serapis*. Your proposed roster and the preparations you have undertaken on my behalf are, in my admittedly uninformed opinion, well judged.

Perhaps I might request a small favour. My youngest son, a Mr. Embleton Hall, happens to be an exceptional amateur naturalist with a passionate interest in the flora and fauna of the Arctic regions. Felicitously, I see that you have not yet filled all your berths. Mr. Hall will report aboard 7 June by midnight. He eats but little, and although he is of a melancholic and somewhat mercurial disposition, if you leave him to himself he will cause you little trouble.

I know I need not remind you of the heavy weight of responsibility that accompanies the privilege of command. Like all of your crew, the wellbeing of my son is now in your hands. I fully trust you will acquit yourself accordingly.

Sir Francis Hall
Ashfield Manor
Caterham on the Hill, Surrey

✲ ✲ ✲ ✲ ✲

28 May 1850

TO: Sir Francis Hall
Ashfield Manor
Caterham on the Hill, Surrey

Dear Sir,

Certainly, Mr. Embleton Hall is welcome to join the *Serapis*. I look forward to making his acquaintance. No doubt you will find it a comfort to have a family connexion aboard ship, to act as your agent and protect your interests.

Sincerely,

David Maxwell

✲ ✲ ✲ ✲ ✲

TELEGRAPHIC MESSAGE: Sir Francis Hall to David Maxwell (29 May 1850)

IN NO INSTANCE SHOULD EMBLETON HALL BE CONSIDERED MY AGENT ABOARD SHIP STOP HE JOINS YOU IN HIS CAPACITY AS NATURALIST ONLY STOP YOUR ORDERS

COME FROM ME STOP FIND CAULDERSON EXPEDITION STOP FIND THE PASSAGE STOP

* * * * *

Ship's Log
8 June 1850

Being the official record of the first sailing of the ship Serapis, under command of David Maxwell, Captain. Log kept by Captain Maxwell (and First Mate Lew Taylor in the captain's absence).

Under sail at 05:00 as scheduled for the first voyage of the *Serapis.* Stored, provisioned, and fully equipped for twelve months' service in the Arctic regions. 31 good men aboard. Weighed anchor and, with a fair, fresh breeze from the East South East, proceeded to sea, then steering a course west by south. All well.

* * * * *

Naturalist's Log
8 June 1850, 11:43

Being the record book of Mr. Embleton Hall, Ship's Naturalist, Serapis.

Confined to a godforsaken floating coffin with disgusting slugs for companions – for a year! The constant motion might be bearable, if not for the creeping damp, the dank smell, and the noise of the idiot men. Most excellent, Father. I shall die of tedium instead of – other things. Well done: it is, indeed, a more respectable death.

Oh look! A *larus canus.* And there! *Mus musculus*! Fascinating. I must carefully document each sighting. What an excellent naturalist am I! And how extraordinary the natural world; how very worth a year of one's life.

⁂ ⁂ ⁂ ⁂ ⁂

Captain's Log
8 June 1850, 21:15

Being the personal and private observations and thoughts of David Maxwell, Captain, Serapis.

Strange to write this log as captain. Strange to *be* captain, come to that. I was never –

Well underway now. The departure proceeded entirely smoothly. Crew seems to be settling in, although the unusual aspects of the mission have led to some first-day nerves. Most seem glad to be back at sea and happy in their duties. Time will tell. Taylor works endlessly and earns the men's respect for it. One hears his steady voice in every corner of the ship, at every time of day and night. He was an excellent choice for first mate. His easy confidence puts any lingering trepidation the men may feel to rest.

The blasted naturalist crawled aboard at 04:30 looking like death itself was dragging him and disappeared below into his quarters. I've not seen him since. I have misgivings as to his fitness for duty, among other things, but Sir Francis, after all, has final authority.

I never thought to be at sea again. It is some impossible mixture of delightful and strange and nightmarish. No one aboard knows of my personal connexion to our mission, but the crew shares my dedication to the cause. There appears amongst all a determination that whatever human efforts can achieve to promote our success will not be wanting. God grant that we find him alive and well, and also his crew.

⁂ ⁂ ⁂ ⁂ ⁂

Told by Ugalik, who became a powerful angakkuq in the years following the first incursion:

There was great discord among us when the creatures came out of the sea in their wooden boats. Some said they were agloolik rising up from under the ice to help our hunters in the long night, and therefore to be trusted. Others said they were qalupalik who had learned to disguise their green skin and wild hair, come to steal the children away. We watched them as they walked about with lumps of wood in their mouths, breathing smoke; they spoke in a tongue that nobody understood. All of us were afraid of what their coming meant to us.

Chapter Two:
June – August 1850

Ship's Log, Serapis
10 June 1850

All well. Weather continues fair and winds brisk. She's a snug little ship, and performs well; Sir Francis's men did a fine job with the construction and equipage. We make good progress. Crew in fine spirits.

* * * * *

Captain's Log, Serapis
11 June 1850, 03:30

Cannot sleep. Always, there is something twisting inside me – and the dreams.

* * * * *

Captain's Log, Serapis
13 June 1850, 01:00

Five years on land have made me soft; I am sore and miserable. Who am I, to command these men? I'm barely a sailor at all anymore.

I thank Providence for my choice of Lew Taylor for first mate: he works ferociously and the men love him for it. He tells me he has a sweetheart at home, that he is affianced to a lovely young thing with a demon for a father, and that he is constantly worried for her welfare. He buries himself in work, he says, so as to exhaust himself and be able to sleep. I wish I could do the same.

* * * * *

Ship's Log, Serapis
13 June 1850

All well. Crew issued double measure of spirits tonight at Taylor's request. Weather continues fair; winds lightening. The northern route has thus far been kind. On track to make a record quick crossing.

* * * * *

Naturalist's Log, Serapis
13 June 1850

Oh, God. I do not know if I can – It is too much. Everything is too much I cannot think

I need –

* * * * *

Surgeon's Log, Serapis
14 June 1850

General health of crew excellent. Four admissions to the sick list since departure (appended); afflictions of no greater importance than those generally resulting from sailors' indiscretions on shore.

Though I've not been to sea for a number of years, I've quickly remembered how I relish it. Bracing, when one has grown soft and fat in London. Little call for medical services as of yet; I pass the days reading up on Arctic scurvy, bush fever, dysentery, a variety of dermatoses, tularemia. I pray this knowledge will not be needed.

Personal aside: although my acquaintance with Embleton Hall is slight and confined only to the scientific circles in which we ran in London, I am not easy in my mind about his health. In the few years I have known him, I have never seen him look as he does now: so pale, thin, and trembling. He keeps much to himself, and looks unwell when he does appear above deck – rather less frequently than I would advise. I have heard him call out in the night, quite incoherently. As far as I can ascertain, he makes no effort to fulfill his duties or to contribute to the work of the ship. I must speak to the captain, although I hesitate. He, too, suffers from some unnamed condition that keeps him up nights, pacing the decks. I fear this ship sails under a cloud and the men begin to feel it.

⚬ ⚬ ⚬ ⚬ ⚬

Ship's Log
15 June 1850, 23:00

The air hangs heavy; the heat is oppressive even at this late hour. Little wind. Crew restless. A storm approaches: a first test.

⚬ ⚬ ⚬ ⚬ ⚬

Captain's Log
15 June 1850, 23:30

Have just had the strangest encounter.

Not an hour ago, I lay sweltering in my bunk trying to sleep. Failing to sleep. A terrible sound came to my ears: a sort of low, broken moan drifting through the dividing wall of my cabin. At first, I thought I had fallen into a nightmare, so like was it to the way the dreams always begin. But the inevitable flames did not appear. I was not asleep. The sound continued without cease for several long minutes.

My cabin is located beside that of the ostensible naturalist, Taylor having given it over in favour of a smaller cabin nearer the crew bunks. I hesitated to intrude upon Mr. Hall, for I've barely said a word to the man in my life. As there is little enough privacy aboard ship, it is usually kinder to ignore the strange habits of our fellow creatures.

The pitiful sound went on and on. It was not loud, but somehow that made it more terrible, that it was mine alone to witness. Finally, I could bear it no longer. I rose and dressed, and knocked on Hall's door.

Silence met my rap, but I persisted. "Hall," I asked. "Are you ill? Shall I send for Carruthers?"

Silence. I hesitated. I did not wish to shame the man, but nor did I wish him to suffer.

"Come for a turn on deck. These cabins are stifling; the air will do us both good."

More silence.

I shrugged. Some men are solitary. I am so myself.

I turned to return to my cabin, resolving to speak with Carruthers in the morning. As I did, something crashed against the inside of Hall's door. The sound of shattering glass and muttered curses followed.

I cried out in surprise and wrenched open the door.

The cabin was dark and smelled of the brandy that dripped from every surface. Glass crunched underfoot.

"Captain Maxwell," a low voice said from the darkness – and how that voice shook. "Apologies – for disturbing you. All is well, sir. Please go."

I found it prudent to listen to the timbre of the voice, and not the words; the voice did not wish for me to go.

"All is not well," I answered firmly into the darkness. "Come. We'll take a turn on deck and I'll call the boy to mop up this mess."

There was silence from within.

I did not wish to order him, but how to get the man out? And then I had a thought: "The storm birds are out in numbers tonight," said I. "Perhaps you'd care to observe them – in your capacity as naturalist?"

A thin, pale face appeared from the darkness. Sweat covered his brow, and his reddish hair hung down in greasy ringlets. He shook so hard his teeth rattled in his head. I was shocked at the state of him, but then understanding crashed upon me: I had seen this affliction before. His eyes were unfocused and he swallowed convulsively. "I was a naturalist once," he said uncertainly.

"Come now," I said, taking his arm as if he were himself a battered storm bird that might startle away in an instant. "Up we go. The air will do us both good."

He allowed me to guide him to the ladder and up the hatch to the main deck. Again I took his arm and we walked the deck for half an hour or more in silence. I believe the air *did* do us both good. We stopped at last, and leaned against the rail, looking out into the night. In the moonlight, his skin was nearly translucent; his extensive constellation of freckles matched the stars above us.

"I'm not drunk, if that's what you're thinking," he said to me, when he noticed my close observation. "I'm not at all well, but I will be soon."

I nodded. "You will. Another week, maybe two. The worst of it will pass."

His head whipped around and he gaped at me. It was as if he had surfaced from a dream, and his eyes were suddenly bright and sharp and shocked.

"You're not the first cocainist of my acquaintance to come over ill after leaving port." I lay my hand on his trembling shoulder. "It really will pass. Not the worst way to make a clean break, all said."

He shrugged and turned away once more. The air began to cool a little and we were refreshed.

"It was your father's idea, I suppose, for you to come aboard?" I asked after a time, for I was curious about our patron.

His face darkened, and he turned on me savagely. "Whatever he is to *you*," he hissed, leaning close to my ear, "Sir Francis Hall is nothing to me – less than nothing. You'd do well to remember it."

He shook off my arm and stormed away. He was below deck and holed up again in his cabin before I could think to follow him.

So. Sir Francis has saddled me with his drug-addled son, and I am drawn into some strange family intrigue.

* * * * *

Naturalist's Log
15 June 1850, 02:00

Briefly on deck. Humiliating.

* * * * *

Ship's Log
16 June 1850, noon

At 04:00, with a great crack of thunder, the storm broke. For hours, the gale continued to increase in force, and nothing was wanting to heighten the wildness of the tempest. From the onset of the gale we were utterly unable to contend against it. It being directly foul for us, we continue to make much leeway drifting to the south west.

✲ ✲ ✲ ✲ ✲

Naturalist's Log
17 June 1850

The noise these birds make is fit to wake the dead. It is by no means certain that I will survive this.

✲ ✲ ✲ ✲ ✲

Ship's Log
20 June 1850, noon

No mitigation in the force of the storms, which rage furiously, and with terrific squalls, rain, hail, thunder and lightning at intervals. Continue to drift at the rate of from fifty to sixty miles a day to the south west.

✲ ✲ ✲ ✲ ✲

Captain's log
21 June 1850, 13:00

If ever I hoped to sleep at sea, these storms have put an end to it. The men labour mightily but there is no way to fight it. When the storm is finished with us, we will be released, and until then we must simply endure.

Sometimes when I am very tired, I forget myself. I turn my head, expecting orders. But he is not here, and *I* am to give the orders. It is strange – terrible and strange. For so many years, his word commanded my actions, his character commanded my loyalty, and his wisdom, my trust. I am as battered and adrift as our own ship without him.

Hall has been up on deck several times. He is miserable and avoids all interaction with the men, but I know he makes a mighty effort. I met his father only once in person, but even on that limited basis I can see a curious similarity that suddenly diverges, like a forked tree branch. What is the cause of their enmity, I wonder?

✲ ✲ ✲ ✲ ✲

Ship's Log
22 June 1850, noon

At 08:00 this morning when in lat. 45°. 34' S., long. 37°. 28' W., it suddenly fell calm. The lull of the tempest was of short duration, and it appeared to have acquired fresh power during this temporary cessation, for the next hour it again blew with its accustomed violence. We sustained considerable damage on our upper deck on the night of the 12th; the head and waist hammock netting having been carried away, along with some other minor mischances.

✲ ✲ ✲ ✲ ✲

Naturalist's Log
22 June 1850, 16:00

Wretched, wretched, wretched. Cannot stay below deck for all the churning and tossing about, cannot walk on deck without being immediately drenched in the downpours. One feels as if one has never been dry, never warm, never still. A year of this – God! Perhaps the asylum would have been preferable. Damn my father for persuading me, and damn me for allowing it. Perhaps I am dead already, and this is all I can expect. Christ knows, I've sinned enough to deserve it.

✲ ✲ ✲ ✲ ✲

Surgeon's Log
23 June 1850

The admissions to the sick list have undergone a considerable increase from the almost constant exposure of the men on deck to the fury of the elements. Working the ship frequently requires the whole strength of the ship's company, and the sickbay shares equally with other parts of the vessel, in being wet, leaky, and otherwise uncomfortable. The atmosphere between decks is loaded with moisture and noxious effluvia emanating from so many persons being congregated in a confined space. Conditions are not likely to improve until the advent of more favourable weather. I do what I can.

✲ ✲ ✲ ✲ ✲

Captain's Log
24 June 1850

The duration and power of this storm is quite unprecedented, even to the most seasoned men among us. In the constant heaving of the waves, it is difficult to form an idea of the general state of the ship. The hatches are, for the most part, battened down, dead-lights fitted on, excluding the light from above – ventilation almost arrested, and the decks entirely saturated, the sea-water at times being several inches deep on the lower deck, from the heavy seas which incessantly break over us. Cascades of salt water occasionally pour through the several cracks and crevices in the hatchways, while the ship's timbers, weeping from every pore, moan and creak piteously. It adds largely to our misery.

The men begin to fear – as indeed do I – that the continuance of the tempestuous weather might so far delay us in our voyage as to prevent our reaching the ice in time for active operations this season.

✲ ✲ ✲ ✲ ✲

Ship's Log
25 June 1850

Weather has finally abated. Once more under the influence of the long-looked-for Trade wind, and making all haste to correct our course. Crew fully engaged in speeding the repairs as well as our resources enable us.

✲ ✲ ✲ ✲ ✲

Naturalist's Log
25 June 1850, 13:00

The worst of the storm seems to have passed, and with it, much of my own physical discomfort. It does so help to be dry.

Throughout the long period of these gales, the storm birds were our constant companions, a plague of intolerable, grating screeching that left no one in peace: sooty albatross (*Diomedea fuliginosa*) and fulmar petrel (*Procellaria glacialis*) in greater numbers than I would expect to see this far north. Either pressed by hunger or emboldened by the fury of the storm, they flew constantly within a few feet of the ship, darting almost with the celerity of lightning at the slightest object they saw floating on the water, and uttering that remarkable shrill noise so peculiar to the storm birds of the ocean.

I wonder –

⁂ ⁂ ⁂ ⁂ ⁂

Captain's Log
2 July 1850, 23:00

Confound Embleton Hall, confound his father, and confound every inclination I ever had to sail after confounded William Caulderson!

⁂ ⁂ ⁂ ⁂ ⁂

Naturalist's Log
2 July 1850, 02:30

Devised a scheme to bait a hook and float it astern with a piece of corkwood attached. The birds seized upon it with voracity, and in this way I procured one of the large wandering albatrosses. When conscious of being caught, he immediately dived, and on rising with wings expanded to their utmost extent, threw himself partially on his back, thereby adding increased power to the great surface of resistance presented to my efforts in hauling, and by this means bent the hook, which finally escaped from his mouth, and was drawn on board perfectly straight. The bird rose proudly, shook his head, and flapping his wings as if conscious of success, betook himself to flight.

I subsequently caught two of these creatures with no little difficulty. Measured at 10 and 11 ft., weighed 19 and 21 lbs. respectively. They were magnificent-looking birds; plumage was white, with a mottled grey back, undercarriage, wings, head and legs of a pink colour. They ejected a large quantity of yellow oily matter (sample collected for analysis), as if sickness had suddenly supervened on their change of element. Samples acquired.

Captain Maxwell, I think, is entirely too preoccupied with observing inane superstitions. Otherwise, he is quite interesting.

⁂ ⁂ ⁂ ⁂ ⁂

Captain's Log
3 July 1850, 08:00

Have just had a lengthy discourse with Mr. Embleton Hall as to why it is not politic to kill and dissect albatrosses while aboard ship, particularly following weeks of gales. Of all bloody things, why he would select an *albatross* is beyond me – and to lure it in full view of the crew, and with such exuberance! The man claims to have no knowledge of naval tradition (and certainly none of Coleridge), great though his understanding of zoology and biology is. It is hard to credit, but he seemed in earnest. He scarcely acknowledged my reprimand and carried on with his dissection; it seems he plans to catalogue the stomach contents of Arctic fauna throughout the voyage to some arcane scientific end, and may God have mercy upon our souls. He is a most interesting person; it will take some delicacy if the crew is not to throw him over the side before we reach land, and with some reason. Had Taylor issue the men a double ration of spirits.

He looked better, though. If not exactly well, at least better, brighter. The influence of the cocaine is passing, and I am glad of it. He must have partaken most habitually for its cessation to have such an effect on him.

⁂ ⁂ ⁂ ⁂ ⁂

Ship's Log
5 July 1850

We have discovered that during the storms, water found its way into the bread-room. As soon as circumstances admitted, its contents were brought on deck for survey. No less a quantity than 986 lbs. was condemned as unfit for use and thrown overboard. This would be a great loss under any circumstances, but particularly in ours, for we lack the luxury of a reprovisioning stop. We shall have to make do and stretch what we have. As long as we are careful, we will not starve.

* * * * *

Ship's Log
21 July 1850

Disaster has again befallen us. At 06:30 (Taylor being the officer of the watch) a squall from the west-south-west suddenly took the ship, which carried away her fore and main top masts, and top gaunt masts, together with the jib-boom – a direful casualty under the circumstances of our position. All hands were called to shorten sail and clear the wreck. Luckily for us the squall was of short duration, and the wind subsequently, for a short time, fell light.

The spars with the rigging attached were hanging over the ship's side, and four of our men in their activity and zeal, had got out on the jib-boom before this was carried away (which it was subsequently to the topmasts) and with it were precipitated into the water – the ship pitching heavily at the time. All the crew were in immediate activity to save their messmates, our smallest boat manned in less time than it takes to write it. They were found clinging tenaciously to the rigging attached to the spars, and were soon picked up under the bows, having fortunately sustained no injury, only the discomfort of their temporary submersion.

Several whales had appeared about the ship, and were still close to us, spouting with a loud blowing noise their graceful curves of water into the air. We became somewhat anxious for the safety of the little boat, as one of those huge monsters rising under her keel, or a stroke of its powerful tail, would inevitably have capsized her; she regained us, however, in safety. During the remainder of the day, all was bustle and activity in repairing the damages. Nothing could exceed the zeal with which our men work, and Taylor first among them.

* * * * *

Ship's Log
4 August 1850

Repairs at last complete, and we begin to make good ground in what has been a difficult crossing. We knew the northern route would pose challenges; it certainly did so.

In the course of the day, we exchanged colours with two American whalers, which were apparently full and homeward bound. Several whales were also seen spouting at a distance, and the carcass of one floated past us, with myriads of sea birds regaling themselves upon its flesh.

* * * * *

Naturalist's Log
4 August 1850

Extraordinary stroke of luck! Sailed through a pod of whales around noon, and minutes later a young carcass floated past! In short order I was rowing the dingy out to examine it – imagine the state of it! Entirely uncontaminated by man and touched only by natural processes! With my hinged saw and Cheselden gorget I was able to enact a speedy post-mortem and discovered numerous ulcers of the stomach and a severe parasitical infestation. List of stomach contents appended.

Samples taken from organs and tissues, and liquids acquired when possible. Well satisfied with the day's work; I shall be several days at least in making my analyses. A most welcome respite from the monotony.

✲ ✲ ✲ ✲ ✲

Captain's Log
4 August 1850

Good Christ in Heaven, give me strength to deal with Embleton Hall.

Today we observed firsthand the ample number of giant whales frequenting this sea (which enables us, incidentally, to testify to its excellence as a cruising ground for whalers). Early afternoon we sailed by the putrid, bloated carcass of a specimen which had died days ago – the smell wafted over the deck and disturbed the entire watch.

Hall, the so-called naturalist and actual madman, was instantly into the dingy and over the side, and was soon shoulder-deep in rotting whale flesh, looking happier than I have ever seen him. It took three strong men to finally drag him, half drowned and fully frozen, back onto the ship. I've forbidden him from going below deck until he thoroughly bathes himself; his clothing I daresay we will drag behind the ship for a time.

The man is nothing but pleased with himself; the crew now alternates between horror, annoyance, and incredulity.

I confess I do not know what to make of him. He alternates between pathological lethargy of spirit and wild enthusiasms that are strange in the extreme. He is entirely self-contained and speaks but little to his shipmates, but occasionally he can be drawn out to talk a little about his latest finds and observations. He then becomes so obviously enraptured, one finds it difficult not to be carried along with him.

✲ ✲ ✲ ✲ ✲

Ship's Log
21 August 1850

First issue of warm clothing supplied by Sir Francis for our use: per man, there is one complete suit of blue double milled box cloth, boots, stockings, boot-hose, comforters, mitts and caps; all of excellent quality, and well adapted for Polar service.

The days have now attained such a length that at the hour of midnight we have very good twilight, the sun being but a short time below the horizon.

At 20:00 a sail was observed bearing down towards us. We immediately communicated and greeted the HMS *Consort*. She had just returned from the ice, and afforded us a most unfavourable account of its state and condition, it being quite impenetrable. As she had viewed it from some three or four miles distant, not deeming it prudent to make a nearer approach, we were nothing daunted by the report but indulged in the hope that the reality of matters would prove less appalling than the description. We took advantage of her presence to forward our last letters and dispatches for England, then parted company and proceeded on our course. They informed us that they were regularly supplied by the natives with reindeer and birds, a large number of which was suspended from the rigging. This is a comfort, given the damage the storms did to our stores.

* * * * *

Packet of letters (partial) from Serapis *to London via HMS* Consort, *August 1850*

My dearest Hannah,

You'll be pleased to hear that we've made the crossing with perfect ease, and you need not trouble yourself with that worry an instant longer. All is well – very well – and we now strike north in search of the *Vanguard*. Already two months have passed since we departed London. Another ten and you shall be in my arms again. I miss you so, my darling. Are you well? I pray daily for your safety and wellbeing. I even pray for *his* wellbeing, for if he is well, he will not succumb to his terrible tempers. The crew is a good one, and I have no doubt of our timely return. When I am overwhelmed with thoughts of you, I plunge into work in hopes this year will pass the quicker for it – and Lord knows, there is no shortage of work to do. I know I shall have the sweetest, best reward at the end of it. I dream of you, sitting so prettily amongst your books and your gowns and the many trifles that fill your days, and, my dear, it sustains me. I must go, as our transport ship waits for our letters. I think of you daily – hourly. I do so hope that you are well and happy, but not so happy that you do not miss

Your faithful,
Lew

Addie,

My dear, my own. The last time I was at sea, I had no wife to leave behind. Now that I do – I cannot lie; now that I do, it is harder, for I miss you so. I have no anxiety with regards to your wellbeing or happiness in London, for I know you have within you the capacity to thrive wherever you are, and whatever your circumstances: it is a quality I admire greatly and singularly fail to emulate. I hope your work with the committee continues satisfactorily.

You'll wish to know whether I'm sleeping; whether I eat? The answers are "no" and "yes, some" respectively. My dreams have not abated, and the closeness of my cabin does nothing to aid my comfort. Indeed, being again at sea seems to have rather increased their frequency. Unexpectedly, I've struck up something like a friendship with the ship's naturalist, who seems to be a fellow insomniac. He's a strange consociate – a most unusual man – but compelling. Perhaps "friend" is not the correct word, but we tolerate each other's company passably well.

The mail ship departs shortly, and I must still write our patron a bland account of our uneventful passage.

Before I sign off – a small favour? Lew Taylor has worked himself into a right state over a girl he's left behind – a girl he plans to marry, if you can imagine! It seems the man's found love, and good for him, but the girl's father is something of a tyrant. Write to her, would you, and ask her to call? It would put Lew's mind to rest to know that she has someone in her corner; it sounds as if the poor thing doesn't have anyone else. Do use caution, however: the father guards her most jealously and is not aware of her engagement. Miss Hannah Crawley is her name, of 54 Oxford Street. Perhaps you can add her to your marvelous collection of strays.

All is well, my dear, all is well. All goes to plan, such as it is.

Your husband,
David

Dear Sir Francis,

We have completed our crossing via the northern route with minimal delay despite inclement weather and some damage to the ship. The crew effected repairs, and we are none the poorer for it. The ship sails well, and the crew performs excellently. As yet we have no news of the *Vanguard*, but we could not have hoped to at this early stage of the search. Appended are charts of the crossing, Ship's Surgeon's notes, and full details of all repairs undertaken. In short: all proceeds as well as we could reasonably expect.

If you will forgive my impudence, I wish also to relate that your son regains his health and strength a little more every day, and I have hopes he will soon put the influence of his past indiscretions entirely behind him.

Sincerely,
Captain David Maxwell

✲ ✲ ✲ ✲ ✲

Told by Kumaglak of Salliq when the sky-dwellers appear

The ends of the land and sea are bounded by an immense abyss, over which a narrow and dangerous pathway leads to the heavenly regions. The sky is a great dome of hard material arched over the Earth. There is a hole in it through which the spirits pass to the true heavens. Only the spirits of those who have died a voluntary or violent death, and the Raven, have been over this pathway. The spirits who live there light torches to guide the feet of new arrivals. They can be seen there feasting and playing and dancing together. The whistling, crackling noise which sometimes accompanies the light of the sky-dwellers is the voices of these spirits trying to communicate with the people of the Earth. They should always be answered in a whisper. The spirits are called selamiut.

✲ ✲ ✲ ✲ ✲

Ship's Log
26 August 1850

The Aurora Borealis was faintly seen for the first time tonight, but was much obscured by the dense haze which prevails – it extends fully from N.E. to S.W. The force of a current setting N. 14° W. from 20 to 25 miles a day antagonizes the power of the wind.

✲ ✲ ✲ ✲ ✲

Naturalist's Log
26 August 1850

The temperature of the sea-water fell three degrees in four hours, remaining a few tenths above freezing point, which led us to expect an early appearance of ice; during the same period, the temperature of air fell 31°. Depth of water varies from seventeen to twenty-four fathoms.

✲ ✲ ✲ ✲ ✲

Captain's Log
27 August 1850

We are now daily employed in putting in order and preparing all necessary implements for ice navigation: ice anchors and chisels, hatchets, saws, whale lines, &c. This is an occupation novel to many, including myself. Under Taylor's careful instruction, all have been duly overhauled and got on deck in readiness for use. The crow's nest has been hoisted to its aerial position, at the fore-top-gallant mast head. Taylor has rigged it up with a trap door at the bottom sufficiently large to admit one person, but hooded over at the top with canvas, so as to afford protection from the wind to its occupant, who is generally the ice master. From here, observation can be made of the ice in relative comfort.

Every day we creep closer to our quarry; closer to *him*, and every day I grow more anxious. Hall must see it – for he watches me closely. I have seen him doing it, sitting over a book in the mess and pretending to read. Then too, when I am on deck going about my duties, I feel his eyes upon me. What does he see, I wonder? We walk the deck every night, now, annoying the night watch to no end I am sure. The damned dreams give me no peace. Does he see my weakness? Worse still, does he see the cause?

He's an interesting man: brilliant, I should say. I understand, now, how he fell into the abuse of cocaine, for his mind is relentless, spinning ever quicker and careless of the pain it causes the flesh that houses it. "Sometimes my body falls behind my mind," he explained once, haltingly. "The cocaine helps – *helped* – me to bear it." He did not wish to discuss the matter further.

He must surely be one of the foremost natural scientists our country has produced, for his mastery of his subject appears absolute. At the same time, he has almost no knowledge of or interest in anything outside of it. The Caulderson Expedition was unknown to him, beyond some vague notion of Arctic exploration. I have related to him all the information I have: the probable route of the *Vanguard*, the fraught history of the search for the Northwest Passage, the urgency of their mission, the heroism of Caulderson himself. He asked no questions – but then, he rarely speaks.

Sometimes – more often than not, lately – I wake hoarse and trembling from my dreams to Hall's soft rap on my cabin door. We go up on deck and walk together then. Sometimes we walk in silence, but more often now, he will speak to me of what he is reading: Larson's latest theory of this, or the migratory habits of that. He speaks softly and gravely, as if imparting an important lesson to a recalcitrant child. It seems unlikely that my comfort is Hall's concern, for he is careless of – well, of everyone and everything except his work, for all anyone can tell. And yet it helps. It does help to feel one has a friend.

✲ ✲ ✲ ✲ ✲

Naturalist's Log
28 August 1850

The number of birds appears daily on the increase, driftwood also in greater abundance. The sea appears full of life; I had the dredge overboard, and added to my collection numerous specimens of the crustaceous and acephalous animals. Today we saw two white whales (*Beluga borealis*) and a narwhal (*Monodon monoceros*) going to the westward.

I should not trust Captain Maxwell. I should shun anyone associated with my father on general principle, and yet I have made a close study of him, and I cannot bring myself to believe that he would willfully harm me. At any rate, he's not thrown me overboard yet, so I suppose I owe him a debt of gratitude. Surely in his absence, the crew would have divested itself of my presence long ago.

✲ ✲ ✲ ✲ ✲

Ship's Log
30 August 1850

During the night, the breeze freshened almost to the force of a gale, and the direction of the wind was not favourable for us, but by morning it entirely subsided, with every indication of fine weather to come. All anxiously looking out for first appearance of land – the crow's nest is seldom without an occupant; and as daylight is persistent, there is now no period of true darkness to interrupt our view.

✲ ✲ ✲ ✲ ✲

Captain's Log
30 August 1850

The hour of midnight comes, but I cannot sleep. This is to me the most enjoyable period of the day. All work on board has eased; everything is still and quiet, only the watch on deck. Now, too, the naturalist emerges from below to take the air; he shuns all company except, I flatter myself, for mine. Now all are hushed to silence, save the low murmuring of the wind and the wash of waters from the ship's progress. It is as if we are all taking in a deep, clean breath and holding it together. Poised – for we know not what.

In the long twilight that has taken the place of night, the aspect of the heavens is truly beautiful. A wide belt of refracted light extending along the horizon resolves into its prismatic colours, imparting a degree of beauty I have never before witnessed. The gorgeous and brilliant yet varied tints of colouring could not possibly be surpassed. The moon rises slowly in the same quarter.

At such times, I feel fortunate to be here. Whatever the sorrows of our lives, we are here to witness this great beauty. I tried to impart as much to Hall; he made no reply.

✲ ✲ ✲ ✲ ✲

Ship's Log
2 September 1850

"Land sighted!" came the cry from the crow's nest. Lat. 64° 31' N., long. 60° 39' W. Double ration of spirits issued to the crew.

✲ ✲ ✲ ✲ ✲

Ship's Log
4 September 1850

Difficulties of navigation abound and are much increased by the addition of fog, together with foul wind and currents. We have not even the land always in sight; yet creep along. We now approach the Davis Strait.

✲ ✲ ✲ ✲ ✲

Captain's Log
4 September 1850

It is unlikely in the extreme that the *Vanguard* would be languishing anywhere to the south or east of Baffin Bay, yet now the hunt properly begins and we must be vigilant. Sir Francis himself believes the wreck –

for surely it must be a wreck – to be to the west of Prince Albert Island, and north of the 70th parallel. He explained his reasoning to me and it was sound. I stare at the charts until I go cross-eyed, but it is the man in the crow's nest who really matters now. I would wish to speak to Embleton Hall about the most efficient methods to employ in this search, for his mind is wonderfully methodical, but any mention of his father or his father's interests sets off such a towering rage that he will not speak to me for hours afterwards. I am glad the ship is free of his preferred poisons.

✲ ✲ ✲ ✲ ✲

Naturalist's Log
5 September 1850

Much noisy excitement this morning, as the lookout gave the signal that wreckage had been sighted ashore. Captain Maxwell immediately weighed anchor; the jolly boat was manned and overboard within the hour. I took a place on the boat, of course, with my sample bag and instruments, and we rowed for shore.

Once ashore, Maxwell took off at a run towards the strange structures lying just inland. I'm sure I never saw a man look so terrified; it was most strange. The men followed more slowly.

It was a hike of under a mile. When I arrived, Maxwell was sitting back on his heels, his face very white. There is some mystery here; Maxwell is not as disinterested as he pretends. The structures, as Taylor explained, were nothing more than Esquimeaux store-houses for the products of the chase, containing the bones of animals, with other evidence of the locality having been at one time their camp.

I thought to have a look around. Old traces of habitation still existed in many places, and there is much to be gleaned from the leavings.

The men went to work erecting a mound of earth, in the center of which they placed a board with the broad arrow painted on its surface, and a record of our visit deposited as per usual practice. While this was in process of erection, I proceeded to the opposite side of the point, where I found an indentation of the coast, forming one of its numerous crescent-shaped little bays. I was surprised at the vast quantity of driftwood accumulated on its shore, several acres being thickly covered with it, and many pieces at least sixty feet in length, the trunks of fine trees. I made a hasty examination and collected numerous excellent samples of soil and small flora while the men surveyed the coastline as best they could, their abilities being rudimentary at best.

Material analysis shall take a week, at least. A very satisfactory day.

⁂ ⁂ ⁂ ⁂ ⁂

Captain's Log
5 September 1850, 23:00

I cannot say how my heart leapt to my throat when first I saw those structures on the shore. I thought –

In any case, we have made our first landing with success: Hall obtained many samples and some surveying was completed. The only man disappointed was Taylor, who had hoped to meet and converse with some of the local Esquimeaux. Hall seemed similarly keen, although now that his illness has passed he seems to be keen on an ever-increasing range of subjects.

Our work being completed, we reached the ship in safety soon after midnight. Our return was rendered pleasant by contemplating the magnificent appearance of the sky to the westward, tinted as it was by the most brilliant crimson I ever beheld.

⁂ ⁂ ⁂ ⁂ ⁂

Ship's Log
9 September 1850

Davis Strait is now behind us and we enter Baffin Bay, plotting a direct course to Lancaster Sound but keeping close enough to shore that any wreckage or debris will be immediately obvious to us. Supplementing rations with fish as much as possible; we must ensure our remaining stores will see us through the winter.

✲ ✲ ✲ ✲ ✲

Captain's Log
11 September 1850

Around 18:00 the lookout espied an encampment on the shore. I know it cannot be our quarry – not so soon, nor so easily. I cannot allow myself to think otherwise; I cannot allow myself to hope. There is no debris in sight, and nothing to suggest a wreck. Taylor expects an Esquimeaux encampment; we have seen dozens of figures through the glass. The men talk with a strange, half-fearful bravado at the prospect of encountering the natives. Tomorrow we shall launch the jolly boat and see what profitable information these strange fellows might have for us.

✲ ✲ ✲ ✲ ✲

Captain's Log
12 September 1850

Launched jolly boat by 07:00 with a dozen men aboard including Taylor (acting as interpreter) and Hall (as naturalist). When about fifty yards distant from the shore, the boat grounded, and a surf, heavy for the

Polar Sea, broke over her, which obliged her to be carried to shore on the backs of the men.

It was then a walk of just over two miles to the encampment. As we approached, we were surprised to see only two men and a woman walking out to meet us. The huts, six in number, appeared deserted.

The men commenced to utter the most discordant yells and threats to deter us. We made friendly salutations with extended arms, but instead of recognition, we were greeted with wild gesticulations and more angry denunciations than before.

Hall and I, being the first in our procession, moved towards them, I carrying my gun. But we found they would hold no intercourse, or allow us to approach nearer, unless we removed our guns, for which they appeared to entertain a great horror, and no less dread of the ship, to which they frequently pointed. The guns were at once placed on the ground, but that would not satisfy them. I then handed mine to one of the men a short distance behind me, with no better result. They still resolutely repelled any advance until the guns were placed about one hundred yards distant. I was not easy in this arrangement, but upon Taylor's strong recommendation, complied.

Having given them proof of the friendly character of our visit, of which we again in words assured them, at the same time presenting a piece of tobacco to each, the whole aspect of affairs underwent a complete and sudden change. The Esquimeaux approached, I am happy to say, without rubbing noses, and in their altered expression and demeanour evinced a desire at once to cultivate friendly relations. They allowed us to examine their bows and arrows, and by our desire fired at a mark – a piece of driftwood fixed in the soil about eighty yards distant. They elevated their bows in an instant without apparently taking aim, and pierced its center, affording us ample evidence of what good targets we should have made for such unerring marksmen.

We then offered them several gifts with which they appeared greatly delighted: a little scarlet and blue cloth we gave them was particularly valued. As we conducted these transactions, more Esquimeaux appeared from the huts where they had apparently been hiding. One by one they came, with greater or lesser expressions of disquiet. We did our best to put them all at ease.

* * * * *

Surgeon's Log
12 September 1850

There was a woman amongst them who attended a young man who moved about by hopping with the aid of two sticks. Through Taylor's translation, I was informed that she was the second wife of the chief, and that the son suffered from an injury received in hunting. His mother at once came forward and removed his moccasin, as well as a piece of skin which quivered his leg. She used a degree of care and gentleness not always seen in my own profession. I was shocked at the appearance which this poor fellow's limb presented – the foot and lower part of the leg being in an advanced state of mortification, filthy in the extreme, and the only covering was a piece of hard skin. As the disease would inevitably be attended with the loss of the limb, and very likely of his life, I was anxious to get him on board, that it might be at once removed with the view of saving his life. This proposition they declined with extreme horror. I, therefore, recommended what was best to be done, but with little hope of its being attended to. In time, no doubt, he will be a victim to the savage custom of his race, described by Taylor. As soon as the tribe leaves the encampment for a trading or hunting excursion, the parents will take him to the summit of the highest land in the area, and there leave him to perish. From the parental care I saw manifested in this case, I am unwilling to believe they would subject him to such a fate, but after all one cannot foresee the actions of savages.

I was unable to ascertain with any degree of accuracy, what were the prevailing diseases among them; cutaneous diseases and chest afflictions appear the principal, as may be inferred from their filthy habits and rigorous climate. I saw several old people afflicted with chronic bronchitis and asthma. They all appear to suffer more or less from opthalmia – in the old people it is very common, with inversion of the eyelids. Several appear to have lost their vision from opacity of cornea – the result of frequent attacks, produced by the combined influence of snow and sunshine. I saw none labouring under any form of congenital disease or deformity, and from what we could learn, there is seldom any mortality except amongst the old people and very young children; resulting in the latter, I should say, from the effects of exposure. When famine exists or accidents occur, of course the case is different.

✲ ✲ ✲ ✲ ✲

Naturalist's Log
12 September 1850

These Esquimeaux! They are extraordinary. Their ingenuity in constructing implements of war and the chase, in preparing skins so as to render them waterproof, in the building of huts; the perseverance and tenacity no less than the success with which they follow the chase. Their powers of patience and endurance of cold and hunger are unequalled by any other race on the face of the globe. There is much I would learn from them.

Their dress is formed of reindeer skin, but they wear the fur next the body for added warmth. I observed tattooing on the chin of the women: a series of dotted lines extended from the lower lip to the chin, forming one band about an inch in breadth. Its meaning is as of yet obscure to me, but must carry great symbolic weight.

At their request, we adjourned to one of the huts, where we found a large fire of driftwood burning in the center of the floor, on which were pieces of reindeer's flesh being cooked, but as black as charcoal, our visit having evidently led to its being neglected. Here we learned the following intelligence through the medium of Taylor's interpretation.

The elder of the two men we first met was the chief of the tribe, and the younger was his son; the woman his second wife, as polygamy exists amongst them. The chief wore a stunted beard, and a moustache represented by a few grey hairs, conveying to me the idea that he had seen some fifty winters. The ship having been observed yesterday, her appearance had caused the utmost consternation amongst the community, which numbers in all about fifty. They reside at this place throughout the year and do not go inland where their enemies reside.

As I stood at the fire next to the old chief, I observed a button suspended from his ear, worn as an earring, which, on examination, I found to be a flat metal button of English manufacture, with the word *London* stamped in a circular form on its inner surface. I immediately directed Captain Maxwell's attention to the circumstance, and inquiries at once began as to the mode in which it came into his possession. Taylor, looking quite startled, conveyed the intelligence that "an Indian like ourselves," as they said, had traded him for it. The name of Indian is applied to all people dissimilar to themselves, and Taylor concluded it could have been a European, but this was impossible to determine from their inability to compute time with accuracy. The chief said, on being questioned, it might have been last year, or when he was a boy, but on this point we could not ascertain the truth and were left in a state of painful anxiety, Maxwell especially. I believe I could have winnowed more information out of the man, but Maxwell was not disposed to "fritter away time."

✲ ✲ ✲ ✲ ✲

Captain's Log
12 September 1850, continued

Intolerable to think that we could have been near to Caulderson – could have been standing in his very footsteps – and not have known it. I questioned the chief repeatedly, until Taylor bade me to stop in the interest of continued good relations. No success; the man had a mind like a child or an imbecile. He could tell me nothing of value. It was all a colossal waste of time, and Caulderson could even now be freezing to death; starving to death alone on the ice. We must hasten our progress.

A mound was discernible about 100 yards inland from the small village, in which a pole was placed and a piece of animal skin or some such thing suspended from its top. Taylor pronounced this a probable grave, possibly of a European; I confess, this statement staggered me. I bid Hall conduct an examination, he being trained in the art of close observation and analysis.

⚬ ⚬ ⚬ ⚬ ⚬

Naturalist's Log
12 September 1850

At the Captain's request, I examined a small mound of rocks perhaps 100 yards from the village. I brought the lame Esquimeaux out with me, half carrying him along, for he struck me as being remarkably quick-witted and useful. I believe Taylor was correct that the mound is indeed a cairn, but it seems unlikely to me that it holds the remains of a European. It is clearly old – far older than 5 or even 10 years. It was constructed as a solid mound, but the elements have tumbled it down somewhat, and the sharpness of the hide marker is much eroded by wind and weather. No scavenging animals were in evidence – not even traces of past incursions. Moss and pale lichen have covered much of the surface rock, their growth undisturbed. My companion was amazed by the attention I paid to the stones and the earth, not understanding their importance to us. We devised a rudimentary system of gestural communication between us and he showed me how tall he was when the cairn was built: no higher than my waist. Whoever lies there, it is not our man.

When I imparted this news to Maxwell, I feared he would faint, so pale and sickly did he look. He put his hand on my arm and thanked me – but would not look at me.

⭘ ⭘ ⭘ ⭘ ⭘

Ohotkto tells of the coming of the qallunaat to the land of the Netsilingmiut:

One day during the summer, two men were fishing at Oweetee-week. When the men looked out to sea they could see a large black thing, not an animal, far out to sea. They had never seen such a thing before and were much alarmed, so they returned to the place where they lived and told the others.

The people gathered in the dance house to discuss the matter and the annatko gathered his charms and his white cloak of caribou belly, to hide and protect them for they were very precious. He took a large deerskin and pegged it to the west wall of the house, had all of the lamps extinguished, then crawled behind the hide to talk to the spirits. All of the spirits said that the men had seen qallunaat, and that these were friendly.

None of the seal people had ever seen a qallunaat, but the wife of Archnaluak, who was named Kakekagiu, had heard many stories from her sister who lived in the southlands: that the qallunaat had given the Inuit many fine presents of wood and iron, that they were very rich in all of the things which the seal-people most lacked.

The next day, the Great Spirit brought the qallunaat to a very good place, near Sarfak where the Tuunit ruins are. This place was later called Qavdlunarsiofik. But then the qallunaat stepped out of their umiak and the people were afraid. Some said that the Great Spirit would destroy the people if they did not kill these strangers, but Kakekagiu spoke to the annatko and together they overruled them.

They decided to hide all the people in the dance house and to send Niungitsoq out with his wife and son to see what the white men would do.

A group of twelve white men marched in from the sea. Two of them came forward and stopped. The other white men came up and laid their weapons on the ice, and then the Inuit put down their knives and harpoons, and soon all were embracing and dancing together.

The Inuit brought the qallunaat to their lodge and shared meat with them. There was one who could speak our language, but his words were like a child's. We found that they were simple minded. They would not eat our meat, and asked strange and rude questions. They made the men furious, but Kakekagiu showed us that they were like children and must be pitied. They had no skins or furs to protect them from the cold. Soon winter would come and Negafook would drag them away to their deaths. When they saw this, the men began to relax. These strange child-men could not hurt the Inuit.

Chapter Three: September – October 1850

Ship's Log
15 September 1850

In our slow progress north through Baffin Bay, we have for two days run alongside a large island, the temptation of which induced some of us to forego sleep and explore it. From the great number of seals visible on the shore, we concluded that fish were plentiful; and, with a view to procuring provisions, we filled the jolly boat with fishing and hunting gear, and a party of us proceeded to the shore. Upon landing, we kindled a huge fire of driftwood; some commenced preparations for fishing, while others proceeded to explore the island, and took our guns in expectation of encountering some of the numerous flocks of ducks that had been observed. The party returned to the ship by 02:00 well supplied with fresh game.

✲ ✲ ✲ ✲ ✲

Naturalist's Log
15 September 1850

Went to land briefly this evening. Found the island to be chiefly composed of sand, shingle, and driftwood; the beach was sloping, with the greatest elevation near the water, from the pressure of the ice forcing up the sand. It was quite devoid of verdure – a few tufts of saxifrage and stunted grass the only trace of vegetation. The pebbles were of granitic character, with porphyry, clay-slate, mica-schist, ironstone, &c., all smooth, and much water-worn.

Further inland, the little island was rich in fossil remains, chiefly corallines (encrinites and pentacrinates). The upper surface is composed of small stones and pebbles, with coralline ledges closely cemented to each other; and the rock beneath, which is composed of granulated, bituminous limestone, emitted the distinctive odour when struck or fractured, and some was plentifully studded with garnets. Numerous uni- and bivalve fossils, chiefly species of Cyathopyllum, Turbo, Bucdnum, Orthis, and Terebratida, were likewise strewn on the surface, presenting good specimens of calcareous petrifaction. It was a relief to exercise the cataloguing capacities of my mind, however slightly.

Maxwell and I walked inland a little; this companionship seems to have become a habit between us now. I rambled – my God, how I rambled. I heard my voice in my own ears, but could not seem to stop. I have not felt myself since I boarded the ship; it was such a relief to be away from the horrid, stinking close quarters. His eyes exhibit unusual levels of central heterochromia: green and blue, grey and brown, with flecks of gold. Most unusual and very subtle; one must look closely to even perceive it. I shall think on how to properly catalogue the colour.

✲ ✲ ✲ ✲ ✲

Captain's Log
15 September 1850

Hall and I walked inland for an hour, perhaps more, while Lew Taylor and a few men (Pine, May, Thompson, and Wynniatt) stayed fishing by the shore. We found two crania of whales, saw traces of foxes, and came on the recent track of a bear, where he had been feasting on the body of a seal but a very short time before. These we followed (at Hall's insistence) in the hope of meeting with him, as they were the first traces we had met with, but he had evidently gone to the ice. We came upon what appeared to be a well-trodden bear path, which led us to suppose this island was a frequent resort of these hoary denizens of the north, with whom Hall longs to have an encounter. Despite the danger, I confess to being rather eager myself.

The ship receded as we walked; first the shore, then the men's fire was lost beyond the horizon.

It was the most alone we've ever been, and we both felt it. He spoke freely, and in a way that made me aware of how constrained he is aboard ship. I've rarely heard him speak more than a sentence or two together, previously! Does he fear his father's influence there, even at such a distance? I wonder, but did not ask. I had no wish to spoil his happiness in that moment, so rare is it.

He had no such compunction about myself, I was amused to find; the man rattled off questions about my life in London and my thoughts about this or that as easily as breathing, all the while stooping to collect samples and examine flora. He knows much about Addie now, and about my naval service. Nothing whatever about Caulderson, of course. Still, he now knows more about me than almost any man alive. I do not speak so freely, as a rule, to anyone of my acquaintance. There is something in him that inspires my confidence. I told him as much; such freedom of speech is most unlike me.

He said nothing to that, surprisingly, but simply handed me a bit of raw garnet that he'd scavenged off the ground, saying roughly that it was in excess of his scientific requirements. A lovely little stone it is: specks of gold mottled with green and blue, grey and brown, and hints of warm depths within. I shall keep it for my watch chain.

As it was approaching midnight, we retraced our steps towards the boat, the blaze of the huge fire burning brightly in the distance.

I feel myself on dangerous ground. I am not, I think, a very good man.

⁂ ⁂ ⁂ ⁂ ⁂

Ship's Log
18 September 1850

We continue slowly up Baffin Bay, eyes always to the coastline. Nothing of any consequence to report; we are becoming initiated into the routine. The weather maintains a pretty favourable character.

⁂ ⁂ ⁂ ⁂ ⁂

19 September 1850

TO: Miss Hannah Crawley
54 Oxford Street
London

Dear Miss Crawley,

Please forgive me for taking the liberty of writing to you without a formal introduction, but our situations are themselves unusual. I believe we have an acquaintance in common aboard the vessel *Serapis*; I am Captain Maxwell's wife, and Lew Taylor's friend.

I have lately received a letter from my husband – the last, in all likelihood, before his eventual return to London – and in it, he passed along Mr. Taylor's hope that I would extend my hand to you in the spirit of friendship.

It is my joy to so do. I feel quite strongly that we women left behind are a sisterhood of necessity, Miss Crawley, but it is just as well to turn such necessity into a pleasure.

Won't you please come to tea? Come as soon as you like – tomorrow? The day after? I should so very much like to meet you.

Most sincerely,

Mrs. Addie Maxwell
23 Little Eastcheap Street
London

* * * * *

Asuilaak tells the legend of Sedna
At Qikiqtarjuaq, two moons after the great storm

Once there lived on a solitary shore an old man with his daughter Sedna. His wife had been dead for some time and the two led a quiet life. Sedna grew up to be a handsome girl and the youths came from all around to sue for her hand, but she would accept none of them. Finally, at the breaking up of the ice in the spring, a great fisherman came from lands far distant and wooed Sedna by offering her father a great cache of dried fish. Her father could not resist and sent his daughter away over the sea with the strange fisherman. When at last they reached the home of the fisherman, after a long and hard journey, Sedna discovered that her husband had deceived her. When his foot touched land, he transformed into a fulmar. Her new home was not built of beautiful pelts, as he had promised, but was covered with wretched fishskins, full of holes, that gave free entrance to the wind and snow. Instead of soft reindeer skins, her bed was made of hard walrus hides and she had to live on the miserable fish which the other fulmars brought her. In her despair she sang:

Aya.
O father, if you knew how wretched I am
you would come to me.
Aya aya aya
O come and take me back home.
Aya.

When a year had passed and the sea was again stirred by warmer winds, the father left his country to visit Sedna. His daughter greeted him joyfully and besought him to take her back home. The father, hearing of the outrages wrought upon his daughter, determined upon revenge. He killed the fulmar, took Sedna into his boat, and they quickly left the country which had brought so much sorrow to Sedna. When the other fulmars came home and found their companion dead and his wife gone, they all flew away in search of the fugitives. Their cries of rage and anguish can still be heard.

Having flown a short distance, they discerned the boat, and with their wings they stirred up a heavy storm. The sea rose in immense waves that threatened the pair with destruction. In this mortal peril, the father offered Sedna to the birds, flinging her overboard. She clung to the edge of the boat. The father then took a knife and cut off her fingers. Falling into the sea, the fingers were transformed into whales. Sedna held onto the boat more tightly, but her hands fell under the sharp knife and swam away as seals; when the father cut off her forearms, they became walruses. At last, with a great blow to her head, Sedna fell away entirely and sank under the waves. She lives there forever, commanding the sea creatures that are born of her body. That is why the hunters sing songs to her and why the liver of the first-killed seal is always returned to the sea.

✲ ✲ ✲ ✲ ✲

Ship's Log
20 September 1850

At 06:00, "ice ahead" was reported from the crow's nest – soon after which many an eager eye was directed to the white line, then visible on the northern horizon; and as we advanced towards it, the sea presented an aspect truly novel to many of us, as the detached masses of ice, in form most picturesque, majestically floated down in our direction. As we stood on, the breeze gradually became much lighter, and the temperature fell several degrees. The masses of loose ice became more numerous, and in proportion considerably greater than before. Large pieces coming in our course were cleft by the ship, producing a slight shock, a grating noise, and an equally strange sensation amongst us, as the fragments having been partially submerged were dashed on either side, while the breeze bore us steadily along. The main pack soon became visible, and as chilling as its aspect was, we hailed it with a cheer. It was reached about noon, in lat. 72° N., long. 75° 11' W.

⁂ ⁂ ⁂ ⁂ ⁂

Captain's Log
20 September 1850

The ice certainly presents a formidable appearance; its lofty, impenetrable barrier extends across our path in a line from N.W. to S.E. This, Hall assures me, is much heightened by the refractive power of the atmosphere, together with the uniformity of surface which ice generally presents from the fragments not being entirely clear of each other. Although it looks forbidding, it may be quite navigable, what is termed "loose sailing ice." This, however, can only be determined by a near approach. We tacked to and fro until the edge of the pack was reached, which was much more distant than we at first supposed. The mass lost nothing of its heavy impenetrable character on actually reaching it. For the rest of the day, we continued tacking along its edge.

⁂ ⁂ ⁂ ⁂ ⁂

Naturalist's Log
20 September 1850

Numerous herds of walruses (*Trichecus rosmarus*) lie grouped together on the large detached masses of ice. The depth of water which they frequent varies from 24 to 37 fathoms. Astonishing ignorance on display: men, having never seen them before, speculate what they could be. Must remember to tell David; he has a pleasing appreciation for idiocy.

⁂ ⁂ ⁂ ⁂ ⁂

21 September 1850

TO: Mrs. Addie Maxwell
23 Little Eastcheap Street
London

Dear Mrs. Maxwell,

Thank you so much for your kindness and hospitality yesterday. I did so enjoy myself at tea! As I mentioned, I lead an exceedingly retiring life and do not often go visiting, and so it is particularly delightful for me to have met such a charming new friend. Your work with the Women's Suffrage Committee is fascinating; it was a great pleasure to hear of it.

Thank you, too, for the loan of the books. I read Mrs. Stanton's small pamphlet this morning, and have now begun Mrs. Fuller's. I confess to some confusion when she writes, "There is no wholly masculine man, no purely feminine woman." I'm sure I am very stupid, but this sounds to me like a misapprehension of the natural order of things. We do not have literature of this sort in our household; please forgive me if my views are uninformed. For all that I've read every book in my father's library – and some several times over – I have never come across such radical and interesting ideas. I greatly look forward to discussing them with you further.

Most sincerely,

Hannah Crawley
54 Oxford Street
London

⁂ ⁂ ⁂ ⁂ ⁂

Captain's Log
21 September 1850

We follow the trending of the pack in loose sailing ice in the hope of making our way to the north; but numerous are our disappointments, as taking advantage of every opening that was presented, we followed its course only to be arrested by the impenetrable pack.

At times we came heavily in contact with detached pieces through which we could not force our way. On the first occasion when it became necessary to send some of our men on the ice to assist us, great was the rivalry manifested as to who should first touch its surface; but after a considerable display of agility, the honour was claimed by the Boatswain.

* * * * *

Ship's Log
22 September 1850

Temperatures fell to freezing point for the first time. Throughout the day it varied much, together with the sea water—from eight to twelve degrees. Light ice formed on deck and in the rigging, although the navigable season in these regions is considered to extend well into this period, and in some years much later.

* * * * *

Ship's Log
23 September 1850

Early this morning, a gale blew in from the south west, which brought us in sight of the coast, to our great relief. We soon approached the land, which presented the appearance of a continuous bank of shingle, having an outwork of dark rocks here and there along the water's edge. On the coast northeast we observed several mounds, into each of which poles were inserted. At first, we supposed them to indicate provision depots left by Caulderson's crew, but Taylor thought they must instead be graves, it being the custom of the local tribes of Esquimeaux to mark their places of sepulture in this manner.

At 13:00 the ice was reported as extending right across our path, but sufficiently loose to sail through. On approaching, we found it a stream of floe ice detached from the main pack, but forming an ineffectual barrier to our progress. We entered it with a fine breeze, and a crowd of canvas, and after receiving sundry hard knocks, and inflicting destruction on all the decaying fragments that came within our reach, we again entered clear water, and altered course more to the north yard, following the line of ice.

During the remainder of the day, we sailed through a field of loose ice, but as the breeze had fallen light, our progress was much diminished since the morning. We anxiously looked out for the land, which we had previously lost sight of; towards midnight it could be discerned from the mast-head, the low point far in the distance, but still indistinct from the fog then rising on the eastern horizon.

✲ ✲ ✲ ✲ ✲

Captain's Log
24 September 1850

Hall requests – nay, demands – that we drop anchor for a day and row to shore to examine the Esquimeaux graves. I have explained the urgency of the mission, but my refusal rankles. He is cold and angry. Cold: yes, he is cold. Saving a life must always take precedence over the study of the dead, regardless of how unlikely he deems our success.

Perhaps he has no interest in his father's mission, but I would have hoped he would trust my own judgment as captain.

Vain hope.

⚬ ⚬ ⚬ ⚬ ⚬

Naturalist's Log
24 September 1850

Several whales (*Balcna Mystketus*) and seals (*Phoca Vituhna*) were seen during the day, and depth soundings varied from 14 to 73 fathoms to a seabed of mud and sand, with broken shells at intervals.

The captain refuses to return to the Esquimeaux graves observed yesterday; this though our supply of game and fish runs low and we must stop soon, regardless. His focus on this Caulderson man is almost an *idee-fixe*, and his interest in everything else is peripheral. It begins to impede my own work. Unacceptable.

⚬ ⚬ ⚬ ⚬ ⚬

Ship's Log
25 September 1850

The wind has entirely forsaken us. We lie becalmed, surrounded on all sides by loose ice, in which there is every probability of our being beset, should a fresh breeze not come to our rescue.

⚬ ⚬ ⚬ ⚬ ⚬

Ship's Log
26 September 1850

We lay all night with all our canvas set, hanging sluggishly from the yards on the glassy surface of a sheet of water some two or three miles in diameter, apparently ice-locked. Masses of snow-white ice, in form resembling little islands, were interspersed around, with intervening spaces of water. There was light sufficient to display the outline of each as they floated motionless on the surface of the sleeping sea. The distant and uneven pack all around, forming a land-like but ice-locked boundary, resembled one of our own northern lakes in its wintry garb. There a vivid imagination might readily have taken a flight far from the Polar Sea, in contemplating the icy scene which surrounded us, the novelty of which was only surpassed by its beauty.

It was our object to sail north, but the obstacles which then presented themselves were of no ordinary nature. A light air had sprung up that compelled us to tack to and fro in the narrow channels between the floes. It soon afterwards freshened considerably, and ultimately increased to the force of a moderate gale from the south-east, accompanied with rain and sleet. Our situation then became critical, as the wind was blowing off the land, and aided by currents, it brought all the loose floe ice down on the main pack. We feared – with good reason – we might become beset. We therefore took advantage of the breeze, and took our course to the east-north-east, through heavy, loose fragments, but were soon obliged to tack to W.S.W, owing to the obstruction offered by a great field of impenetrable ice, which might have been our destruction. We continued working the ship close-hauled, alternately to the N.E. and N.W., endeavouring to make progress north and get clear of the perilous position in which we were placed, from the rapidity with which the ice was then setting down on us.

It was quite appalling to observe immense floes coming on towards us. Some fragments were impossible to avoid, and as the ship struck them from time to time, the shock was tremendous, and vibrated through every timber of her solid framework – even endangering the safety of the masts. It was only by great effort that anyone could maintain his equilibrium on deck. Towards midnight we found ourselves in more open water, and observed the floes less numerous. At this time, the loom of land was reported from aloft.

✲ ✲ ✲ ✲ ✲

Captain's Log
27 September 1850

The point is moot now, I suppose, for we have left Hall's precious Esquimeaux graves far behind us, of necessity if nothing else. I cannot afford the luxury of attachment; I cannot allow myself to be blinded, or turned. It is the same terrible conundrum –. It is the same. And now I add hypocrisy to my other sins, for what cared I for my captain's orders when –

✲ ✲ ✲ ✲ ✲

Ship's Log
28 September 1850

In the course of the morning, the wind quite died away, leaving us again becalmed, surrounded by heavy ice and drifting to the northward. In an effort to reposition the ship in an open channel of water, all our available boats were at once called upon to tow – the first time we have had recourse to this tedious operation – leaving only a few men on board to work the ship along the narrow and tortuous channels through which we wended our way. All cheerfully lent their aid, wherever it could be available, to facilitate our progress and free us from our difficulties.

The boats were of great service, and never did men work with more zeal or energy. Nor were we less occupied on board, it requiring the exercise of all our skill, not only in the steering, but in tacking and trimming almost incessantly to keep clear of the ice, with which, despite our best efforts, we frequently came in contact. We thus continued our slow advance throughout the day.

About two hours later, we had cleared the limit of the ice, and joyfully hailed our return to open water.

We were greatly relieved to have escaped from the perilous position we had been placed in during the preceding days; and as it was the first time we had come in actual conflict with the foe, we had good reason to be pleased with ourselves.

It was generally remarked that the character of the ice was much heavier than that generally met with at this time of year.

✩ ✩ ✩ ✩ ✩

Captain's Log
28 September 1850

It was back-breaking work towing the ship through the slim channels in the ice – and it went on and on, seemingly endlessly. Hall was the first on the jolly boat. He refused rest, refused meals, and worked harder than all the others; I do believe he made up for his weeks of idleness in a single day. And over the course of many hours, whenever our work brought us into contact or whenever he caught my eye, he looked at me with such disdain, with such a faintly sneering expression, as if to mock the men's passion for our mission, and my own. It makes me rage to think of it even now. I was obliged to turn my back; I don't know what I would have done.

✩ ✩ ✩ ✩ ✩

Naturalist's Log
29 September 1850

The water has gained in temperature but steadily decreased in density, having fallen from 1012 to 1008 in twenty-four hours; and it has likewise become brackish and discoloured from the admixture of fresh water flowing from the numerous tributary streams along the shore.

As the sun touched the icy horizon towards midnight, it presented the most splendid appearance I have ever witnessed, and one on which the naked eye could barely for a moment rest, owing to a dazzling brightness surrounding the disc. It was free from those gorgeous and varied tints I have previously noticed, and now presented one vast sheet of silvery flame, illumining the horizon with a degree of magnificence to be seen in no other region of the world. The reflection of the sun's rays on the snow-white surface of the ice is a sight that goes far to compensate for the intense misery of sailing here.

The captain and I did not speak today. Now he has gone below, and I walk the deck alone.

I miss his company. I miss him.

* * * * *

30 September 1850

TO: Dr. Barnabas Brown
#9 Harley Street
London W1

Dear Dr. Brown,

I write in haste; I know you will forgive my abruptness. Papa has had one of his episodes. Despite my best efforts I provoke him dreadfully, and at last I could not pacify him. It was a most terrible night.

Please come when you are able. He has locked himself in his study and will not listen to reason. He has not slept. I fear what he will do next.

Humbly yours,

Hannah Crawley
54 Oxford Street
London

* * * * *

Naturalist's Log
30 September 1850

Another day. Dull, dull, dull. Water and sky. The captain avoids me. My mind – it is not pleasant. Nights like this are the most difficult to bear without my usual respite. Perhaps father was correct in his estimation of my character. I have not wished to admit it; I have done my best to avoid the thought, to prove him wrong. Yet always I come back to this: the asylum doctors were correct to confine me, for something inside me is terribly wrong.

* * * * *

1 October 1850

TO: Mrs. Addie Maxwell
23 Little Eastcheap Street
London

Dear Addie,

Thank you for your kind invitation. I should like nothing more than to pass the afternoon in your charming company, but I cannot come to tea. Papa has had a terrible attack. The doctor says I must not leave the house until my arm is healed, in perhaps two or three weeks.

Your affectionate,

Hannah Crawley
54 Oxford Street
London

* * * * *

1 October 1850
TO: Hannah Crawley
54 Oxford Street
London

[By return post]

Little Hannah,

Oh, my dear girl. I am so very sorry. Of course you must stay home. Listen to your doctor, and heal well. I shall send my maid over directly with a parcel for you: an excellent salve for drawing out bruises, a poultice for your arm, and perhaps a book or two to divert you. I'll instruct it to be placed in your own maid's hands; we certainly do not wish to alarm your father. Have her watch for it at 7:00.

Your friend,

Addie Maxwell
23 Little Eastcheap Street
London

* * * * *

Ship's Log
1 October 1850

About 05:00, having reached within three miles of the shore off of Lancaster Sound in an area known as Possession Bay, we saw an object on shore which we thought was a beacon. We immediately launched the jolly boat and pulled steadily towards it.

The morning being cold and foggy, we had a long and cheerless pull to the shore. On reaching it, we found the island to be about three miles long, and about half that breadth entirely composed of sand and shingle with great quantities of driftwood strewn on its surface, which, together with the combined action of the ice and currents had doubtless led to its formation.

✲ ✲ ✲ ✲ ✲

Captain's Log
1 October 1850

As we approached in the boat, I fancied that I saw two figures in motion but distance and the fog then present did not enable me to speak with certainty; nor did anyone else aboard see anything. I could feel Hall's eyes upon me, and turned away. I cannot trust my eyes, maybe, but if it had been Caulderson or any of his men, they would surely have approached us.

We made land and walked to the beacon we had viewed from the ship, finding it to be nothing more than a small pile of rocks and driftwood with a spar, about twelve feet long, placed vertically in its center. It was tumbled down almost to the point of total destruction, but it left no doubt in our minds of its being the work of human hands. The question was, were those hands civilized or savage? There were none of the expected signs of European influence here; for if Caulderson had left a beacon, he would presumably have left a food cache and a written record of the expedition's progress. Here, we had only scattered stones and worn hunks of wood. Esquimeaux, then: another cairn worth nothing to us.

The men and I started to move away, muttering about wasted time, but Hall, lagging somewhat behind, suddenly fell upon the cairn with a cry.

He presented an astonishing spectacle, crawling about upon his hands and knees, then examining every inch of the spar with minute care. He ignored the rest of us completely; he may not care a whit for our mission, but give the man a puzzle to solve and he cannot resist.

After a time, he came away from the beacon and examined the area surrounding. He was particularly interested in a large piece of ice, some twelve or fourteen feet across, which, from the effects of pressure, had been forced on the beach. I could make nothing of it, but Hall examined it closely with his glass, sometimes stopping to pick at it with a gloved finger.

I set the men to work digging out the cairn, of curiosity if nothing else. Then I joined Hall at the ice.

"Observe, captain," he said at last – the first words he had spoken to me in days. "This is old ice. The surface has the appearance of being trodden on. It is compressed, but smoothly so, as if by a skin slipper: not a European boot, which leaves a distinctive tread. The cold has preserved its appearance. Beneath the compression points are things you should recognize: what is this?" he asked, pointing to a small grey lump in the ice in his hand. I took it up in astonishment.

"Hall! Surely this is an oat?"

"Oh, well done indeed!" His words were mocking, but his voice betrayed his own pleasure in discovery. "*Avena sativa*: the common oat. I suspect even *you* are aware that it is not a native plant to these shores. Caulderson, or perhaps some of his men, were here – I cannot say when, but certainly not recently – and left a cache of food that has since been disturbed and removed. If you would care to look over this piece of ice, you can see other fragments of evidence confirming this observation. Traces of wheat flour, even, here and here."

"Show me."

We spent a good half of an hour kneeling there, Hall revealing incontrovertible evidence that the so-called beacon or cairn had in fact been a cache left by Europeans.

Then he rose and began to walk in slow circles, expanding outward from the site of the ruined cache, his eyes trained on the ground. His circle widened until he was out of our sight. I did not accompany him. The men, now used to Hall's eccentricities, returned to their work.

Not half of an hour later, there was a familiar shout in the distance. We raced across the island to find Hall kneeling, once more, in the dirt. A scrubby clump of moss campion covered an exposed rock, and Hall was pulling it apart with careful fingers. Wedged alongside and half-overgrown was a bundle of brown rags, so hidden that I cannot imagine that any but his keen eyes would have seen it.

"Here is something that has been discarded as worthless, whether by human or animal hand, it is impossible to determine," he said, as his careful fingers retrieved it, "but I daresay you will see some value in it."

He thrust it into my hands and turned away. I strove to still the trembling in my hands. It was a little sheaf of papers, rolled up and wrapped in rags, and bound with a bit of cord. By what miracle it now rests with me, I cannot say. But then again, perhaps that miracle is nothing more or less than the skill of my friend, Embleton Hall.

* * * * *

Told by Inookie, who was there at Qallunaataqhiuvik when the qallunaat first came:

That first night, everyone was scared, not knowing what was in our hunting territory. We all gathered in one of the tents with quite a few of our shamans. Qiqtutumuaruq was the most powerful shaman, and when he went into his trance, he told us that what we had seen were qallunaat. He said, "We do not have to be afraid of them." Next morning it was very clear and beautiful weather, and so we decided to walk over. The shaman had told us the qallunaat were not dangerous, not to be scared; they were people.

One man said, "We should war with these people," but the other Inuit said, "If we war, we will not win. As long as they're peaceful people, not violent or aggressive, let's be the way they are. We won't lose any men and they won't lose men either." Just in case something went wrong, we took along our long spears with blades of bone and antler.

As we got closer, these big people emerged from the ship and we Inuit lined up. They probably were expecting something worse, so they were ready. The shaman told us, "Maniktumiq. Smoothly, not aggressively."

The Inuit all stood together and said the same word: "Maniktumiq. Maniktumiq." It was a prayer to a greater power; a prayer to the spirit. All together we began walking gently and smoothly, not aggressively.

Many of us were frightened. We didn't want to give in to these people because we didn't know what they were. Because they weren't quite Inuit. And their clothes – how they dressed! They had no sealskins or caribou hide. We had never seen clothes like theirs. Eventually we decided the qallunaat were dressed in rags, because we knew their clothes could never protect them from the cold. We wondered, "Why are they dressed like that? It's very cold; their clothes are not fit for this kind of weather." We thought, *perhaps they are ghosts who cannot feel the cold.*

⋄ ⋄ ⋄ ⋄ ⋄

Record deposited by Captain William Caulderson
Of the HMS Vanguard
27 August 1846

Herewith are deposited full records of the voyage of the HMS *Vanguard en route* to discover the Northwest Passage to the Orient, and further to explore the Northern Arctic regions and claim the territory for the glory of Queen Victoria and her imperishable British Empire.

As documented in our three previous caches (location coordinates appended), the voyage out has thus far met with great success. As an additional method of leaving record of our having gone along the coast, for any other ship that might follow us, I ordered that the word *London* should be stamped on a series of small copper buttons, to be distributed amongst the local Esquimeaux far as our resources could effect it. Any subsequent ships may discover these upon meeting the tribes, and thus know of our prior claim to the territory.

Our progress to the eastward has been much retarded by baffling winds and currents. We seldom now average more than twenty or thirty miles per day. It may therefore be easily supposed how ardently we hope for a leading wind. We put to land at this site just under a fortnight ago, hoping to replenish our stores of game and of the scant wild leaves which the Esquimeaux have shown us to act as mildly effective antiscorbutic agents – particularly vital as our lime ran dry after our first year.

Certainly, the most interesting aspect of the journey thus far has been the Esquimeaux. Since we do not have a naturalist with our party, I shall note down my own inexpert findings here. Luckily, our present encampment has allowed us to develop strong relations with the local tribe, which appears to be intelligent and cheerful.

Their clothing is almost universally composed of deer-skin. The lower garments are sometimes continuous over the feet and legs; but more generally, the boots are separate, with a coat or jerkin covering the body, ending behind in a peak. A hood is attached to the coat, which is the only head-covering they use. The dress of the women is made sufficiently capacious to allow of their carrying their young children (for whom they appear to entertain much affection) either in the hood, or in contact with their skin, and they manage to do it very adroitly. Polygamy exists among them, when the women are sufficiently numerous; the number of the wives depends on the wealth of the husband and his ability to maintain them. They appear to be bound by stronger bonds of affection than is usually observed among savage nations, but their standard of morality is evidently low, and a husband will gladly traffic with the virtue of a wife for purposes of gain. I have strenuously opposed the inclination of some of our men to take advantage of this moral weakness, but have not always been successful, human nature being what it is. Repeated instances of this were evinced in our intercourse; and no feeling of jealousy appears to exist amongst the Esquimeaux. The women do the greater part of the out-door work, except hunting and fishing; they, however, enjoy a higher position and more consideration than is usual amongst savages. The women manifest affection for their children but the father appears to be stoically indifferent. They are not a prolific race from all I could learn, and male children are ever more welcome than females.

They have no idea of numbers, more than what is represented by the fingers, nor can they express their ideas of time in any other way than by the indications afforded by moon and sun, which are vague and unsatisfactory.

Being desirous of ascertaining their stature, they readily submitted to our measuring them, which appeared to afford them much amusement. They give ample evidence of the muscularity and strength of their limbs; and certainly I never saw firmer, more compact, or much better formed specimens. Their hands, notwithstanding the great amount of manual labour to which they are subject, are beautifully small and well formed – a description equally applicable to their feet; and their teeth, white and regular, were displayed to considerable advantage in the hearty laugh in which they frequently indulged. Both sexes are tattooed on the chin, having a vertical line about half an inch broad in the center, extending from the lip, with a parallel but narrower one on either side of it, a little apart.

The men are keen and expert hunters, and afford ample evidence in their appearance, look and movements, of being possessed of all the essentials to ensure success in the chase. When so much depends on the result of their exertions, it may readily be imagined how keenly the perceptive faculties are exercised. Nothing short of their existence as a race amid the dreary wilds of their abode depends upon their success. In regions where nature is so sparing of her gifts, I need not speak of the enduring patience, hardships and privations, which this enterprising hardy race are compelled to undergo, along the inhospitable, snow-clad coast of the Polar Sea.

Upon first landing here, my lieutenant initially had concerns how we would protect ourselves from the Esquimeaux, in case they should take it into their heads to act in aggression. Their numbers were great enough to do us significant mischief. We had, therefore, to teach them to regard us and ours with the greatest respect, and at last we hit upon a method of accomplishing this. A powerful mine was buried beneath a snow hut at a good distance from the ship, and a fuse laid from the ship and well covered with snow. When that was ready, we collected the Esquimeaux together by the ship. I spoke to them about the white man's power: that we could spread destruction about us, and even at a great distance accomplish the most extraordinary things. It was, consequently, for them to behave themselves properly and not expose themselves to our terrible anger. With a terrific report, the igloo blew up, and clouds of snow burst high into the air. This was all that was required.

Sadly, however, they remain much given to pilfering and cheating when engaged in barter. Numerous instances of their being possessed of both propensities occurred within the first week of our encampment, where their cupidity became much excited by what they saw, and where there existed no moral, controlling power to restrain them. They are much addicted to falsehood, and seldom tell truth, if there be anything to gain by departing from it. Almost everything they see, they make an attempt to steal – chiefly articles of iron from the ship – and when detected, they manifest no sign of shame or remorse.

And yet, nothing can exceed their civility to us. They appear surprised we do not indulge in raw fish as freely as themselves, and are exceedingly anxious that all our party should stay and over-winter with them. They offered us many inducements to do so, the chief one being that they would summon the rest of the tribe to meet us and make merry.

I trust the day is not far distant when the light of civilization will dawn on this poor and benighted, but intelligent race of beings; for it is deplorable to think that there exists in the Queen's dominions people so utterly neglected as they have been, without an effort having ever been made by the rulers of their land (here, the Hudson's Bay Company) to ameliorate their condition, or remove them from a state of heathen darkness. But where monopoly exists, progress is arrested; and it is to be hoped the wisdom of our legislature will, ere long, destroy the one and promote the other, and thus develop the resources of their country to the permanent advancement and happiness of its inhabitants.

And so we bury this letter with a cache of supplies, for our return or for those who come after us, and press north. We shall deposit another cache as future circumstances permit.

We all have regrets; we all have loved ones left behind. We commend ourselves to their fond memories.

They little know our England who deny
The claim we have, from zone to furthest zone,
To belt the beauteous earth,
And treat the clamorous ocean as our own
In all the measuring of its monstrous girth.
The tempest calls to us, and we reply;
And not, as cowards do, in under-tone!

With Freedom's flag uplifted, and unfurled;
And this our rallying-cry, whate'er befall,
Goodwill to men, and peace throughout the world,
But England, England, England over all!

⋆ ⋆ ⋆ ⋆ ⋆

Inookie of Qallunaataqhiuvik continues her story:

After the qallunaat departed, we hurried to see the strange inukshuk they had built. But it made no sense, and the people thought it was another sign of the qallunaat's madness. They had made a great mound and covered it with a piece of skin-that-was-not-skin, and covered that with rocks and then sand and driftwood, and when we uncovered this we found many sacks and hard casks of strange substances.

One of the little casks held some of the small brown squares we had seen the qallunaat burn in their mouths. Ulluriaq started using these as her toys – they were perfectly square. But one day some moisture came in the sealskin tent. As a result, the squares got wet and when we came into the tent, we smelled something foul. We wondered what it was. So we went to where Ulluriaq kept her toys and realized it was those squares. Her father collected all of them and threw them away.

The sacks were full of little crumbling blocks and different powders; we could not conceive of their purpose in burying such things. Ulluriaq and the other children took the blocks and tossed them back and forth until they crumbled to dust. Then the children discovered they could hit the sacks of powder and they would appear to smoke. They beat the sacks until they were emptied of their powders and then gave them to the women so that we could make use of them. They were all having fun – laughing, seeing the smoke blowing in the air. They said, "We have made a new kind of snow!" and the women shook out the last of the crumbs and said, "We have made a new kind of raindrops."

✲ ✲ ✲ ✲ ✲

Ship's Log
2 October 1850

Having discovered Caulderson's cache and the *Vanguard* records by virtue of naturalist Hall's exceptional observational skill, we returned to the *Serapis* and immediately set sail in a northeasterly direction. We now know that we are on the correct course.

⁂ ⁂ ⁂ ⁂ ⁂

Captain's Log
2 October 1850

The letter! My God, what a letter. I laughed to read it, once I was safely in the privacy of my cabin; it was like hearing his very voice in my ear. The supercilious, officious, maddening... It was so like the public Caulderson, the captain, the commander – and so little like the man I know.

But then – his last line…

We must get him back. I believe I see at last how the thing can be accomplished: it is not, after all, as hopeless as seeking a needle in a stack of hay. Hall is the key: Hall and his exceptional natural perspicacity – honed by many years of scientific training. If anyone can find Caulderson, I believe it will be him. I must approach him carefully, for he will not be willing and his temperament is difficult. I will bide my time. Days will pass. I will allow our relations to thaw naturally and return to a state of easy friendship: our disagreement of the last week will surely blow over. And then we shall see if I cannot convince him to offer his assistance.

⁂ ⁂ ⁂ ⁂ ⁂

Captain's Log
15 October 1850

This evening, finally, I quelled my nerves with whiskey and approached Embleton in the twilight hour. The man is susceptible to flattery of his talents and skills; I have noted it many times. And so, I began by commenting on some small task he had completed this afternoon, and making of it an example of his fine observational acuity, which I then took the opportunity to extol.

He rolled his eyes and said nothing, but coloured up charmingly.

"You wish for my assistance in your 'mission' to find Caulderson, do you not?" he asked abruptly.

I am sure I am not a very subtle man, but still he startled me with his perception. "Embleton, I beg you." I took him by the arm, and our positions made me remember our first walk together on deck, and marvel at how we had changed – for now I required *his* help. "If we are to stand a chance at finding him alive and well, we need your active help and participation. The only reason we found the last cache was your persistence and skill. Please. Help me. Plan and strategize with me. Come to my cabin. Examine the charts. Work with me."

He pulled away. "He's not alive, David. Whatever my father made you believe, it is almost certain that he and his men have perished. After five years, the likelihood of finding survivors is almost naught. And even if he were alive – I am not here to do my father's bidding." His voice was tight and ugly.

"That is pride, and it is unworthy of you," I replied, becoming angry myself. "For the sake of some filial animosity, you refuse to help save a life – perhaps many lives? Are you so heartless – so cold?"

His eyes were icy when they turned on me, and I shivered despite myself.

"So I have been reliably informed." His voice was sneering now.

"Put your mind to good use, I beg you. I *beg* you! To the saving of a life!"

He snorted. "Why will you not accept the fact that Caulderson is almost certainly dead?"

I refused to argue that point again. "To the service of the empire, then."

"Certainly not."

I hesitated.

"To me?"

There was a long silence. He turned and walked away.

* * * * *

Naturalist's Log
15 October 1850

He is far from disinterested in this mission, whatever he claims.

Never have I been called generous, or applauded for selflessness: these things are not in my repertoire of feeling. What he asks of me – He does not understand how far outside of my character he asks me to act.

I am not, I think, a very good man.

Chapter Four:
October – December 1850

Ship's Log
15 October 1850

We proceed towards the Barrow Strait in a westerly direction. Progress is slow, but still we hope to reach Parry Sound before winter falls and navigation becomes impossible. Surveillance of the shoreline continues, the duty being relegated to the three or four crewmen with the sharpest eyes, in rotating shifts of six hours each. Fruitless thus far.

* * * * *

Captain's Log
16 October 1850

As the season wears on and winter approaches, the ice makes travel ever more perilous and slow. I dare not push our pace for fear of running up against a berg and damaging the ship, but it is almost unbearable to watch the coastline inch by so slowly. And each night when the temperature drops, I am reminded that *he* must feel the cold even more keenly than we do. What must the prospect of another winter on the ice – a fifth – do to a man? I think on it too deeply, and it torments me – but what is my torment to his?

I no longer walk the decks in the evenings, but keep to my cabins, where it is quieter.

* * * * *

Naturalist's Log
17 October 1850

The nights lengthen and temperatures begin to drop. The formation of young ice is apparently a serious obstacle to Arctic navigation; as I am confined to this ship, I have made it an object of study.

Ice first appears in the form of minute flocculi, which gradually become larger, more opaque and globular, then coalesce. They possess for some time their spherical outline, until pressure identifies them more closely with each other, when a thin film becomes formed on the surface of the water, imparting to it an oily appearance, to which the insipid name of "pancake ice" has been given. This becomes broken up by the slightest contact with heavier ice; and the fragments sliding under, or over each other, acquire greater thickness. From frequent repetition of the same process, and the continuance of low temperature, they soon acquire strength and thickness, become united with others, and form a frozen surface through which a ship cannot possibly penetrate when thus surrounded.

These floes undergo the same liability of being broken up by the pressure of heavier masses. The fragments become thrown up and cemented to each other, forming packed ice, which may go on increasing, together with the accumulation of snow, for periods of indefinite duration, and ultimately present that terrific, indeed impenetrable barrier to navigation so frequent in these seas. Wind is the great antagonistic agent to the formation of young ice; but when this is absent, and the temperature falls, it is surprising to see with what rapidity congelation takes place.

The only interesting person on the entire ship is abstracted and useless, and I? I am reduced to watching water freeze.

* * * * *

Ship's Log
20 October 1850

Our position has not materially altered. On the 18th we drifted a little further to the north, and the morning being very clear, at an early hour the ice mate was sent aloft to report on the relative state of the ice and land – his field of vision embracing an extent of at least twenty miles. No land could be seen directly to the northward in the line of the Strait, but that on the western side bore away to the northwest, and that on the opposite side to the northeast. This is, indeed, very gratifying intelligence – there is now no doubt that we have entered Barrow Strait.

* * * * *

21 October, 1850

TO: Mrs. Addie Maxwell
23 Little Eastcheap Street
London

Dear, kind Addie,

I write again to thank you, this time for your extreme solicitude during my convalescence. I enjoyed the books you sent tremendously, and I greatly appreciate your discretion in the matter.

I'm pleased to report that Dr. Brown has pronounced me fit and well; my arm hurts me hardly at all anymore. I have been given permission to resume my usual activities. I wish nothing more than that I might invite you to call upon me here, but my father's health and temperament proscribe that possibility. Might I be so bold as to call on you tomorrow? I must return your books, and I would so like to hear more about your thoughts on them, and the work of your Committee.

Most sincerely,

Hannah Crawley
54 Oxford Street
London

* * * * *

21 October, 1850

TO: Hannah Crawley
54 Oxford Street
London

(By return post)

Dear Hannah,

Of course you must come tomorrow! Come for luncheon, for tea – what you will. I shall be delighted to see you well – and I do most solemnly promise not to talk shop the entire time. As you are no doubt learning, once I begin to discourse on the movement of women, it is rather difficult to head me off.

Most sincerely,

Addie Maxwell
23 Little Eastcheap Street
London

* * * * *

Captain's Log
22 October 1850

I am constantly striving not to think or speak of things. It has always been a necessary condition of my existence: the knowledge that some things must not be spoken – generally, the most important things. Silence is safest.

Hall and I have grown adept at skirting around our discord, neither abandoning our position, nor wishing to upset our delicate cordial relations. We are not as close as we were. I feel it keenly, but I *cannot* think that he is in the right.

How lonely it is to be captain. I have heard the phrase before, "the solitude of command." ~~He suffered with it, I know, before we – I did not understand it then. I do now. It has been so long since I –~~

[Final sentences redacted.]

* * * * *

22 October 1850

TO: Mrs. Addie Maxwell
Secretary, Women's Suffrage Committee
23 Little Eastcheap Street
London

Dear Addie,

Possibly you have heard the news, but it is worth sharing again: Lord Howard has agreed to submit the petition to the House of Lords sometime in the New Year. As per the resolution passed at the May assembly, I shall draw up the final wording for approval by the Association's executive at the next meeting.

I feel most strongly that the petition must call for the entire enfranchisement of our sex, regardless of birth, property, education, and so on, and must rest upon rational arguments rather than sentimentality. There is a portion of our membership who would have us press our so-called moral advantage, and use the imagined purity and goodness of our sex as the sole argument for suffrage. But that is not equality either. *What we want for women is equal rights, equal admission to all social privileges; not a position apart, a sort of sentimental priesthood*. Casting ourselves as the moral guardians of the nation will do us no good in the future, and only serves to divide our movement now.

The only question of any import is whether it is right and expedient that one half of the human race should pass through life in a state of forced subordination to the other half. Any other question is a distraction from our ultimate goal.

I trust you are yourself in agreement. Anything you can do to sway our more, shall we say, angelic sisters-at-arms to our own understanding in advance of the coming meeting would be most helpful. It would also be beneficial to recruit as many new sisters as possible. Our voice, when it speaks, must be unequivocal.

And now I must beg forgiveness for the businesslike tone of my letter, for I am equally desirous to know: how are you, dear? What news from your wandering husband? What are you reading, and what think you of the new Dickens? (Is it not appallingly dull?) I must come to London soon; I am most desirous to see the new construction in Hyde Park; can the so-called Crystal Palace possibly be as ostentatiously allegorical as it sounds?

Yours,

Abiah Higginbotham
President, Women's Suffrage Committee
37 Upper Hannover Street
Sheffield

✿ ✿ ✿ ✿ ✿

Ship's Log
25 October 1850

The ice floes are now large enough that we are able to secure the ship tightly to the side of a likely specimen and so drift safely alongside. Throughout the night of 23 October we drifted slightly to the southward, and at 05:00 on the 24th we came in contact with a large piece of floe ice, which striking the ship on the starboard quarter, swung her completely round and carried away one five inch halser with a tremendous crash. Although the impact of the ice was violent, happily no casualty occurred. No time was lost in remedying the disaster, and we were again secured to the same floe, with a nine and six inch halser. Soon after this occurrence, another large piece of ice struck the rudder head, which was swung up for the sake of security, about six feet above the water line across the ship's stern, and carried away the life-buoy. Some idea may be formed of the magnitude of the ice that assailed us, from the fact of its striking the rudder head at such an elevation – a repetition of which was guarded against by hoisting it still higher.

We continued throughout the day heading steadily to the northeast. At evening we sighted an island four miles distant, Leopold Island, in all likelihood, and the wind abating, the ice opened as the pressure diminished, and a few narrow lines of water could be seen here and there. This tended to ease its embrace on the ship, and we had got more into the center of the Strait, sounding in from 34 to 62 fathoms water. We lost sight of the island towards the evening, which was a restless and anxious one to all. A quantity of heavy ice frequently struck the vessel, pressing and grinding against her trembling side, but fortunately with no serious consequence.

At 23:00 on the 24th, all being still and silent about the ship, the whole mass of ice to the northward of our position appeared as if under the influence of some wonderful convulsion of nature, and came with sudden and alarming force against the ship's side. All hands were speedily on deck, but entirely helpless as the ice bore down heavily and steadily on us, and pressed us against the floe which had hitherto borne us in safety through such an adventurous course. While it resisted, the ship was elevated nearly two feet out of water, inclining about fifteen degrees to that side from which the pressure came. Had she not risen in this way, she would to a certainty have been crushed. Had the force continued, it must have thrown her broadside on the ice –fortunately it ceased within the space of fifteen minutes from its commencement. Some of us had knapsacks ready for a start, as it lay not in our power to do aught that could avert the danger; and all hands stood breathless on deck, until it again became suddenly silent.

We remained, however, in an anxious, uncomfortable state throughout the night, not knowing the moment when our safety and that of our ship might not be again as suddenly imperiled. We dared not go to rest, but merely lay down with our clothes on and knapsacks under our heads, ready to start on the first sound of alarm. During the middle watch, we had a repetition of the pressure, but less heavy than before. On the morning of the 25th, we found we had been carried to the southward, and had approached nearer the coast: a lane of water had also appeared in the direction of the former, in which a few seals were sporting. So we escaped again into open water.

* * * * *

Captain's Log
25 October 1850

The dreams took me last night, in a way they rarely do. Almost always, once I realize I'm dreaming, I can wake myself and escape. But last night – Flames engulfed me, and smoke filled my lungs. Slowly, the flames took on a monstrous character: screeching and moaning like dying men. I knew it was not real, and tried to wake, bashing my head down again and again, praying I would wake before *he* appeared, as he always does, flames licking his flesh; a scream in his throat. I could not end it. I could not. Caulderson appeared; begging. His features shimmered and shifted, and then Embleton Hall stood before me. I watched in horror as his flesh melted off his face; all the while he screamed and cursed me for my failure, and I was paralyzed with the horror of it. I could not move. Not to save my life, and certainly not to save his.

Suddenly – it was not just him, not just me: the whole world was screaming, rending, shuddering in a deadly paroxysm. I know now it was the vibration of the timbers of the ship, protesting under pressure as the ice bore down on them, the greatest amount of pressure having come on the quarter close to my cabin – but I did not know, then. I rolled, retching, gasping, off of my bunk, covered with sweat and entirely disoriented. The sound persisted: what was dream and what was reality, I could not discern. I shook and shook, and vomited up over the floor.

I know not how long I crouched there, but the next thing I knew there was a hand on my shoulder, and a kind voice in my ear. It was Hall – pressing a clean handkerchief to my face, bidding me rise. He was well. He, at least, was well. It had all been a trick of an unstable mind.

He brought me to his cabin and sat me on his bunk. He treated me with kindness I do not deserve: poured out a generous measure of brandy and helped me to drink it, and helped me gather myself before facing the frightened men above deck. I must not be so weak.

✲ ✲ ✲ ✲ ✲

Naturalist's Log
26 October 1850

I must admit that lying trembling on deck in the middle of a frigid night with 30 other men, listening to thousands of pounds of ice attempt to destroy the vessel, your only possible salvation, is a circumstance which brings the essence of things into stark relief.

The ice has granted me two boons of late: a moderately interesting interruption in the monotony of the voyage, and a resumption of my previous close relations with David, for we spent the night beside each other with nothing to do but converse while the rest of the men somehow snored around us. We spoke of the Indies – of adventures he'd had in warmer climes where icebergs are but a terrible legend for native sailors to tell their sons. He told me what he could remember of the flora and fauna of the region, but he is not a trained naturalist and his memory is imperfect; it was good, though, just to hear him speak. We spent many hours together, but for all that, I could not, through subtle or blatant enticements, persuade him to speak of Caulderson. On that point, he will not budge. He wishes me to find the man, to care about this mission, but he will not give me all the facts. I cannot pull information from the air! It is tremendously frustrating.

* * * * *

26 October 1850

TO: Abiah Higginbotham
President, Women's Suffrage Committee
37 Upper Hannover Street
Sheffield

Dear Abiah,

Delightful news, both from Lord Howard and from you. I shall look forward to your visit with eager anticipation. Please do stay with me? The house has been too quiet since David's been away, and I would love to have you all to myself.

As to the business of your letter. I do, of course, agree with you entirely.

As you know, I can be quite persuasive when I wish to be, and I have now turned all my efforts to the more recalcitrant members of our little association. How they cannot see the dangers and flaws inherent in their arguments is beyond me, but I have my own stratagems, and I make headway.

I do not rage, Abiah. Oh no – you would be quite proud of me. Instead, I smile and I charm. Innocently, I ask, *why* the existence of one half of the species should be merely ancillary to that of the other, and *why* each woman should be a mere appendage to a man, allowed to have no interests of her own, that there may be nothing to compete in her mind with his interests and his pleasure. And then I say, with wide-eyed wonder, the only reason which can be given is that men like it! It is agreeable to men that they should live for their own sake, and women for the sake of men. It is agreeable to them that we learn to think it so natural that we do not question it. It is agreeable to them that we accept some abstract notion of moral superiority, as long as we cede all *actual* power to them. And if this is so, how can our moral superiority – unquestioned, you understand – how can it have any persuasive weight with such self-interested creatures?

And they look startled, Abiah. Some of them physically flinch, and I do feel for the matron who must return home to cook her husband's dinner after learning to see him as her captor for the first time. The thing we must remember is: we are united in a common goal, and women – regardless of the vagaries of their arguments – can never be our enemies. Not even those who oppose our methods most stridently.

And now, that is enough politics for today. *David Copperfield* is dreadful; I refuse to read another word of it.

On an entirely different note: perhaps you've heard of an interesting social establishment just off Covent Garden for men and women of certain libertine attitudes? Far be it from me to corrupt the sanctity of your hearth, Abiah, but I shall stand you a gin at Dukes, and we'll each find a gentleman for the evening, yes? Or have you perhaps come to your senses and changed your mind (again) about other possibilities? Ah, you know I only tease. I sometimes miss the old days.

Mrs. Addie Maxwell
Secretary, Women's Suffrage Committee
23 Little Eastcheap Street
London

✲ ✲ ✲ ✲ ✲

Ship's Log
31 October 1850

Progress has been slow, but we have now made it through Barrow Strait. Towards morning, the wind fell very light, and was succeeded by a calm. Several small spaces of open water opened around us, affording room for the ice masses coming up from the southward to drift more rapidly, grinding against us in their course. Although the temperature remains low, the cold is not so severely felt as on the few previous days, owing to the absence of wind; but everything wears a most wintry appearance and the moisture of the atmosphere rapidly freezing as it falls, gives a coating of snow-white frost to the yards, rigging, and every part of the ship.

As our stores of fresh meat run low, we think it best to replenish while the opportunity exists, and now launch a hunting expedition to a small island in the Strait, listed on charts as Russel Island, but not well known.

✲ ✲ ✲ ✲ ✲

Naturalist's Log
31 October 1850

All my resolutions turned to dust in the face of Captain Maxwell's command. "Come," he said, and I could not refuse; there was such quiet resolve in his voice. The irrationality of it irritates me to no end—but still I agreed without thinking, almost. I really must master myself.

✲ ✲ ✲ ✲ ✲

Captain's Log
31 October 1850

Thank God – *thank God* – that we stopped where we did, and thank God for Embleton Hall. We went ashore mid-morning, the men spreading out in small groups with hunting rifles and snares. Hall and I walked inland a little, but seeing nothing of interest, were soon back at the shore preparing a butchering station to process the meat we anticipated the men would bring back.

We worked together in silence, and it was good to bend our strength to a common task.

The men began to trickle back in the late afternoon. The island being small, most of the kills were smaller mammals: two dozen rabbits, a few ptarmigan, a brace of geese. The last party to arrive dragged a young polar bear between them; they had been lucky to stumble upon him as he bent to drink at a tiny freshwater spring, and it was only because he was so young – perhaps only three years old – that they had been able to carry him at all.

Hall was in agonies that he had not seen the bear alive, but we consoled him with the promise of stomach contents for analysis and his complaints subsided.

Warde, who had bagged the bear in the first place, quickly incised the abdomen and began the butchery, handing off the stomach to Hall with a derisive sneer; I must keep watch on that.

Hall took no notice of him, but turned his back and prepared to make his observations of the organ.

Each man was bent to his business when Hall suddenly gave a startled cry. I dropped my knife and ran to where he crouched in the snow over the bloody organ. He looked up at me with the greatest surprise. "Captain," he said faintly, "here is something you must see."

He dipped his hand into the mess of gore at his feet and pulled up – something – which he held gingerly between his fingers.

"There, do you see?" he asked.

We stared at him, uncomprehending.

He snarled impatiently and thrust it out into Warde's face. "There!" he said, and then brought it to me. "And there!"

"It's a handful of shit," Warde said, and laughed roughly.

"It is," Hall agreed. "And if you believe that is all it is, perhaps you have succumbed to premature snow blindness. For Heaven's sake!" He pulled out his pocket handkerchief and carefully wiped the object clean. Something now glinted in his hand.

"Is that –?" I could not finish my sentence.

He nodded. "A button. A trace of Caulderson, Captain."

Warde snorted. "A handful of shit," he repeated stupidly.

Hall turned his back and continued. "Look here. *London* is inscribed, just like the last we found."

We looked at each other silently.

"They are close," I whispered at last.

He shook his head. "They *were* close. There is nothing to indicate –"

But I did not hear the end of his sentence. Already I was running, running, and calling out orders while I ran, to mount a search: *to find them.*

All the rest of the long day we searched that island from shore to shore. We found nothing.

✲ ✲ ✲ ✲ ✲

Ship's Log
1 November 1850

We have discovered more evidence of the Caulderson Expedition, in the form of a button in the belly of a young bear killed by a hunting party, but as of yet we have not located a landmark or cairn or any evidence of life. Russell Island is too small to support a settlement; we make now for the mainland just to the south. It is visible from the island; if Caulderson and his men were here, they would surely sail for that more prosperous shore. And too, if they were never here, and the bear simply carried the button along with him in his travels, he must have come from that direction, as he could not have swum further.

✲ ✲ ✲ ✲ ✲

Ship's Log
3 November 1850

At 04:00, the ship dropped anchor offshore and a party of a dozen men set out in the jolly boat, but our progress south was arrested by a stream of young ice, which obliged us to make a little detour to the eastward, our pikes proving of much service in testing its strength to bear our weight; and thus we pioneered the way. Within about one mile of the shore we were obliged to leave the boat, for the ice could not easily be broken through, and it bore our weight with reasonable consistency. Here we discovered that the field on which we were walking was in rapid motion, and passed along the inshore grounded floe, in such close contact as to throw up some heavy pieces, packing them together. As it was our object to get on the grounded floe, and so on to the shore, I approached the edge of some young ice to test its capability of bearing us with my pike, when it gave way under me, and I fell, but was quickly picked up by some of our party, with only partial immersion. Ship's Naturalist requested I return to the ship at once, but I did not deem such a precaution necessary, particularly as we were so close to achieving our object. For there on the shore, as if waiting for us, was a landmark built up of rocks and driftwood. It was the work of but a few minutes to unearth the record buried within it. There was no food cache this time, but a small bundle of rags wrapped around a water-tight tin which held a sheaf of papers.

⁂ ⁂ ⁂ ⁂ ⁂

Record of the voyage
of the HMS Vanguard
21 November 1847

It is late in the season for us to be in this position. We have not yet made camp, and the temperature plunges. I write this in great haste, for although time is short, a record must be left.

We dropped anchor at Cape Dundas as per our planned route, and rowed the jolly boat to shore through ice shards and slush. Our goal: to make visual survey of the coast and to confirm the viability of the current route of the Passage. We have been leisurely in our progress thus far, enjoying the novelties this strange land affords; but now we all seem set on working towards a timely completion. In short: we grow tired and our thoughts turn towards home.

After the exercise of some adroitness and activity in our movements, we managed to clamber up the sides of the inshore floe, when the ice was still in process of packing. We computed the distance from the ship to be about five miles. This part of the coast presented a bolder appearance than elsewhere; its almost vertical escarpment was interrupted in several places by deep gorges, and up the precipitous side of one we ascended. On attaining the summit of this cliff, about 150 feet high, we assembled our little party and took formal possession of the land in the name of our most gracious Sovereign, planted the ensign of St. George, and, with three hearty cheers, completed the ceremony by drinking health and long life to our beloved Queen and His Royal Highness Prince Albert.

The men made hasty explorations, and were delighted with the short run they had on land, which they familiarly called their own. We then prepared to ascend the high land, from whence we could complete our survey. Anticipating a hike of two or three hours, we left four men to erect the mound under which we will bury this record, and to prepare dinner during our absence. The general aspect displayed the usual undulating, hillocky character, with the same unvarying sterility and barrenness. The ascent was at first gradual, in the ravines through which we passed; snow had accumulated in great quantity, into which we sunk deeply, rendering it fatiguing, from the efforts required to extricate ourselves.

From the top of the escarpment we could clearly trace the termination of the western land to a headland or cape of considerable elevation, while that on the eastern side trended away to the northeast, with a clear, undoubted field of packed ice, intervening. Everything, therefore, was fully confirmatory of the opinions previously formed, and no doubt could remain as to the existence of a Passage. From the summit of that hill, I felt convinced that the highway to England from ocean to ocean lay before us, and that we were on the very cusp of establishing the existence of a Northwest Passage.

As the temperature did not admit of our remaining long at rest, we commenced the descent, delighted beyond measure at the result of our observations; and, as the luncheon carried in an outside pocket had become so hard frozen that we could not eat it, there was no unnecessary delay.

The hour had grown late, however, whilst we had made our ascent, for in our eagerness we failed to account for the unusual depth of snow. Much fatigued and exhausted from our long march and want of food; yet from the lateness of the hour there existed every probability of our passing the night in the open. As the cold became severely felt, we could not remain at rest more than a few minutes at a time, owing to the rapid abstraction of body heat, and were consequently obliged to keep in constant motion. We retraced our steps over the rugged, slippery course, which it had cost us so much labour to cross but a short time before. It had then become quite dark, and as we were unable to distinguish the unevenness and irregularities of the ice over which we walked, or rather clambered, we fell incessantly. We appeared to have lost due power over our limbs, from the effects of cold and exhaustion, the alteration in the ice, and our intense thirst.

We had advanced about a mile or two, our eyes anxiously directed towards the ship, when we halted to fire our guns, in the hope of receiving some token of observation; but in vain. Again we started – a light was seen hoisted at the mast-head of the ship, but this was nothing more than what might have been expected to point out her position, and did not allow us to hope for any immediate succour. With the increasing darkness, the appearance of the weather had become more dreary and wilder than before – thus cold, hungry, and thirsty, without covering, there was increasing probability of our spending the night away from the ship, and as our small stock of ammunition was well-nigh exhausted, the chances of our being able to attract a party to our position were likewise diminishing. Rockets were seen fired from the ship, and a gun at intervals; but like the light at the mast-head, they afforded us no other comfort than the knowledge of its being done to direct our homeward course.

Our thirst was intense. At last, with the aid of a few matches, the wick that had been immersed in the spirits of wine, and some pieces of paper, we contrived to melt as much ice in our little kettle, as afforded to each of us nearly a wine glassful of water. It seemed a great luxury, although a little brackish. And then we were once more in motion, clambering over the rough slippery ice; with falls heavy and frequent, as it was impossible to see our way clearly in the darkness. Time thus wore on, while we still wandered about, occasionally taking a few minutes' rest, with an irresistible desire to sleep, until the cold compelled us to be again in motion.

After a time, we knew not how long, one man – Jack Simpson, as we later discovered – fell in the snow and did not get up again. By the time we realized his absence, we had walked far enough in the darkness that we could not find him again: this though we made a great hue and cry, and spread out to search as best we could. The driving wind made it unlikely that we would hear his answer to our calls.

In the killing freeze, we had nothing to do but go on, taking careful note of our companions and watching for weakness in their gait.

In the course of the night, two more of our party fell: Jim Cooper and Dr. Lemay. They were dead by the time they hit the ground, eyes already freezing over. We could not carry them, not in our reduced condition, and to stay with their bodies would have cost all our lives, for none of us were immune to the profound cold.

We left them with our prayers and went on. They bore the consequence of my own failure to properly anticipate the requirements of the expedition, and their deaths are on my conscience.

About 03:00, a light could be seen approaching us, and soon afterwards signals were fired in succession from the direction of the shore – a search party.

We stood on the ice, near helpless from the effects of cold, fatigue, and thirst, anxiously awaiting their arrival. When they arrived, we threw ourselves on the ice and hastily partook of some food and a draught of water, the first thing called for; this, by constant agitation, and by being nearly in contact with the skin, they had maintained in the fluid state. This greatly revived us and we again proceeded onwards as rapidly as our exhausted state would allow, falling and tumbling about like drunken men whom we resembled not only in gait, but likewise in speech.

Thus terminates a sorrowful adventure. It is dawn now, and we have attained the shore – all exhausted, frozen, half dead. I am the last man to board the jolly boat. I shall finish this record and commend it to the mound. We have been twenty-seven hours absent from the ship –

walking, I may say, the entire time. The distance exceeded thirty miles, which in consideration of the nature of the ground, was more trying than double the distance over level country; and what with the intense cold of the night, no tents, inadequate clothing, and entire want of food, there was but too much reason to fear that morning would have furnished a much longer list of casualties.

We will press on. We are close – so very close – to the Passage. We will not winter here, but will press on until the ice makes progress impossible and we are forced by God's own hand to stop. In this way, we honour our fallen comrades, our fallen friends.

Jack Simpson
Jim Cooper
Dr. Patrick Lemay

Let them now rest from their labors.

Captain William Caulderson

⁂ ⁂ ⁂ ⁂ ⁂

Captain's Log
1 November 1850

I cannot think of this. I cannot speak or think of what this will have cost him. Nothing I can say can help him now, and so there is nothing worth saying at all.

My impulse, like his, is to push north. Why should we sit and wait for the ice to find us? Are we not men? Shall we not act?

⁂ ⁂ ⁂ ⁂ ⁂

Ship's Log
4 November 1850

Little distance in the past days. There is every appearance of the pack becoming stationary; and no one doubts that our winter must be spent in its grasp. We press on for whatever final distance we can in these last days before winter.

⚬ ⚬ ⚬ ⚬ ⚬

Naturalist's Log
5 November 1850

The calm stillness of the atmosphere affords us a magnificent parhelion from which a zone of pale yellow light encircles the heavens, making a striking contrast with the azure blue and the softened mixed tints of the sky. A faint parasellena was observed yesterday, but was not remarkable for its beauty. Nearly the last of the feathery tribe was also seen – a solitary ptarmigan flying to the south. Several seals made their appearance wherever there was a little space of water to be found, and the stillness of the day was frequently interrupted by the hoarse croaking of a couple of ravens which kept flying circularly about us – the sound, I must say, falling mournfully on the ear.

The captain speaks only in short bursts of commands, and only to Taylor. He looks at me with suspicion, when he looks at me at all, as though I am a snake coiled to strike. I do not know what has occurred that our good relations, so recently restored, have once again soured. I do not understand him at all. Truly, itemizing the stomach contents of a polar bear is less trying than attempting to comprehend David Maxwell.

⚬ ⚬ ⚬ ⚬ ⚬

Captain's Log
7 November 1850

The ice thickens by the day. I fear any hope of finding Caulderson before the winter must be abandoned. I stand on the threshold of a bitter failure.

* * * * *

Ship's Log
12 November 1850

The thickness of young ice has been measured at twenty inches; preparations are now underway for closing in for the winter. We overwinter here: 74° 2' 26.5272" N and 99° 53' 55.2552" W; just to the east of Parry Sound.

Under Taylor's instruction, the crew laid a bed of snow about sixteen inches deep on the upper deck, over which a macadamized covering of sand and gravel was spread, and an embankment of snow about eight feet was built around the ship, both of which contribute greatly to maintain warmth in the interior. Ventilation consists of copper tubes from ten to sixteen inches in diameter, passing through the deck, from the top of which canvas funnels are attached, and conducted through the housing cloth to the open air, to the height of about fifteen feet. These promote a good draught and the free escape of the foul air generated below, as is evidenced in the dense volume of vapour which ever issues from their tops. By this means and from the fact of the men being kept off the lower deck for so many hours of the day, the air between decks is rendered much more salubrious and conducive to health and comfort than it would otherwise be. Carruthers has declared himself satisfied with the quality of the air below deck. Fires have been lighted, including a Sylvester's stove for the general warmth of the ship, a small stove in the sickbay, in which seven pounds of coals are daily consumed, one in the mess-room, where from eight to twelve pounds of coals are burned, and one in the captain's cabin, for which six pounds are daily issued – in addition to which there is the galley fire on the lower deck for cooking throughout the day. The value of fuel in the Arctic regions cannot be overestimated.

✲ ✲ ✲ ✲ ✲

Naturalist's Log
15 November 1850

The agency of gunpowder in blasting ice having been hitherto unknown, and untried in ice navigation, I have today made several experiments with regard to the necessary ratio of gunpowder to size and density of ice in order to result in the helpful and safe clearing of obstacles. The crew was much interested in my little trials. These were attended with success, and afforded pleasing evidence of the powerful auxiliary we have at command for future operations. I have not yet seen Captain Maxwell, but I will inform him of my findings at the first opportunity.

To my great surprise, several of the crew came out on the ice to observe the experiments, and stayed with me even when the wind picked up and the temperature fell in the late hours of the afternoon. Clem Basting was there, watching keenly and even asking an occasional question, although his usual companion Jed Warde was, predictably, absent. So intent was Basting on the results of the experiment that I warmed to him, and ventured to suggest that he can do much better for companionship than that insipid clod. Ah well. By now I am quite used to his disapprobation. The loss is his, for he stormed back to the ship and missed a most satisfactory explosion of ice not ten minutes later.

✲ ✲ ✲ ✲ ✲

Ship's Log
17 November 1850

At an early hour, the sledge with provisions and other requisites for seven men for a fortnight was packed in readiness, but as the state of the ice did not admit of its safe transit for a distance of a couple of miles from the ship, the entire strength of the ship's company was employed for carrying the articles separately over this space. Accordingly at 07:00 all hands were assembled on the ice, and on the word of command, started towards land each carrying as much of the equipment as he could. The party presented a strange and novel appearance as they wended their way over the ice, following the course pointed out by the pioneers, until the rough ice was safely crossed at 08:00, when we halted and repacked the sledge and sent the party on its way. Under Taylor's command, the party consists of Wynniatt, Court, Wilcox, Milner, Basting, and Hall. Their mission is exploratory: to become familiar with the local lay of the land, to scout for any Esquimeaux encampments and initiate friendly relations, and to bring back whatever fresh meat they are able to kill. We wish them Godspeed.

⚬ ⚬ ⚬ ⚬ ⚬

Captain's Log
17 November 1850

Taylor is correct, and I know it. He *should* lead the first party out, and I *should* see to winter preparations aboard ship. Should and will. I was wrong to suggest otherwise, and good on him for holding me to my place.

Christ. To sit and wait at home like a woman – it is intolerable.

⚬ ⚬ ⚬ ⚬ ⚬

Ship's Log
22 November 1850

We who await the return of the scouting party pass the time in various employments. Our first order of business was to form an ice road between the ship and the mainland by first levelling the ice, and then marking the path with poles, as guides. When the party does return, they will have a much easier time of it than they did on departure.

Lowery Smith and young Sykes have undertaken to turn our current stores of frozen meat into pemmican, upon the supposition that frozen meat may be ground up as easily as the more usual method of drying it, and it will require less fuel to cook, as well. Their method is to grind the frozen meat in a malt-mill, and then cook it dry over a low heat; next to mix it with nearly an equal weight of melted beef suet or lard and a small amount of oats. The result could not be called delicious, but it is sustaining.

✲ ✲ ✲ ✲ ✲

Ship's Log
27 November 1850

The travelers returned to the ship at approximately 20:00 this evening.

First Mate Taylor's report:

In the ten days of our little expedition, we made a circuit of the land surrounding the ship to a radius of approximately 70 miles. We found no evidence of Esquimeaux inhabitation, or any other signs of human life. Hunting was also sparse, although we bagged several dozen small hares over the course of the journey, which we gutted and brought back.

Our days began at 07:30, having previously taken what the men were pleased to call 'breakfast' –some pemmican and a little cocoa mixed with tepid water (the spirits of wine not being sufficient fuel to boil it). At 13:00 we would halt, take some biscuit and grog, and then at about 17:30 encamp. This became a difficulty, from the fact of the buffalo robes, blanket sleeping bags, and tarpaulin, being so hard and frozen that on pitching the tent they could not be spread, and thawing could be produced only by the entire party lying on and imparting to them that warmth from our bodies which we sorely needed.

Sleep was rendered but little refreshing, by the cold produced by our half frozen garments, at a temperature varying from seven to fifteen degrees below zero.

The small consumption of food during the journey was quite wonderful: only eighteen pounds of pemmican, thirty-one pounds of biscuit, and eight pounds of oatmeal; and instead of there being a decrease of weight from this consumption, the contents of the sledge upon return actually weighed one hundred pounds more than when we started, from the accumulation of ice on the blankets, tents, coverings, &c., caused by the vapour emanating from our bodies, being rapidly converted into frost, and deposited on everything around. The want of water was most severely felt, as melting the ice generally entailed loss of time; and the quantity of fuel taken proving much too small; the water was consequently limited.

We returned to ship with no casualties to report, and only minor injuries of the sort related to the extreme temperatures we endured.

A rough chart of the area explored is appended.

✲ ✲ ✲ ✲ ✲

Naturalist's Log
28 November 1850

I can affirm that geologizing at a temperature from 15 to 20 degrees below zero is not the most agreeable occupation. It was vital to collect ice and snow samples from various depths, however – absolutely vital – not to mention the ground covering and rock, when I could reach it. The repeated exposure of my hands to the elements caused them to become frost-bitten. My right hand was so severely bitten, and the mischief spread with so much rapidity that on reaching the ship, it was a stiff, frozen mass. I had not the slightest ability to bend it, and on plunging it into a basin of cold water, a thin film of ice formed on the surface. Carruthers is apprehensive of its safety – unduly, I believe. Still, I confess it is not pleasant to be forced to rely on my left hand, and the pain in my right is not insignificant. It has taken me over an hour to write this brief entry.

✲ ✲ ✲ ✲ ✲

Captain's Log
29 November 1850

On 28 November, the sun took his departure. The day was beautifully clear and serene, one of the few fine days we have lately had. There was scarcely a breath of wind, and the temperature fell to two below zero. When the last glimpse of the sun was revealed to us, his rays were most truthfully reflected on the western sky, from whence, shedding their prismatic tints on the land beneath, he imparted an appearance of rare beauty to the scene, where stillness and solitude alone prevailed. Thus commenced the long Polar night of dreariness and gloom.

Everything now wears a truly wintry aspect; snow falls in considerable quantities, and nothing but a uniform white surface meets the eye wherever it wanders. The ship is completely embedded in it, and appears as if she could never move again. A death-like stillness reigns around, in which it is startling in the extreme to hear even the sound of a voice or the tread of a footstep on the frozen surface of the snow. I do enjoy the silence. The slightest incident is gladly seized on as a subject of conversation and comment; and thankful do we feel for the agreeable excitement afforded by the occasional visit of a pair of ravens, the capture of a fox, the pale bright light of the moon, the brilliant splendour of the Aurora, the constant presence of stars, or the meteoric flash of aerolites.

* * * * *

Naturalist's Log
10 December 1850

We are visited almost daily now by two ravens (*Corvus corax*) – it is my fancy that they are the same two ravens we met before. Although they are the most widely distributed of all corvids, I was surprised to see them this far north. I watch them cross the Strait from west to east, and return again in a few hours, always together. They say that ravens mate for life, but the claim is likely nothing but romantic twaddle. Certainly, it is unsubstantiated. The cold must suit them, for they appear to be as glossy and fine as ever. I wish I could say it suits me as well, and strive to inure myself to it, but it is very harsh.

* * * * *

13 December 1850

TO: Hannah Crawley
54 Oxford Street
London

My dear,

It was such a pleasure to see you Tuesday last, and I thank you for your kind letter. I am gratified to hear that your father's health continues fair. When I think of what he – Well, no. I will not start down that road today.

Next week is the December meeting of the Women's Suffrage Committee. The final meeting of the year is something of a celebration: we dine at Simpson's and make merry until the wee hours of the morning, and all talk of politics is expressly forbidden. I should say, perhaps, all *serious* talk, for it is impossible to entirely outlaw the subject from our party.

I suppose you will not be able to stay late with us, but surely we can invent some excuse for your father that will enable you to join us for dinner? Please be my guest? My dear friend Abiah is most eager to meet you, and I believe you would enjoy our fine group of ladies. Do say that you will come!

Your friend,

Addie Maxwell
Secretary, Women's Suffrage Committee
23 Little Eastcheap Street
London

* * * * *

Ship's Log
17 December 1850

It is surprising with what readiness men accommodate themselves to a mode of life, strange and novel to the majority of them. The great author of invention never fails. It is astonishing to witness the number of tradesmen that are to be seen at night, on our lower deck, all actively engaged at their respective pursuits; tailors, bootmakers, and knitters: a great variety of needlework. In fact, anything that a needle is capable of doing is, at least, attempted; and it is no less laudable than strange to observe the progress which ingenuity and industry enable them to make, and the degree of perfection which they ultimately attain, as they are all self-taught. Nor are reading and improvement of the mind generally forgotten; for while thus engaged at work in groups, they generally have the best scholar, as they call him, engaged in reading to them aloud. Thus are the evenings passed, the day being occupied in exercise, and the light duties they are occasionally called on to perform.

✣ ✣ ✣ ✣ ✣

Surgeon's Log
20 December 1850

Hall's frostbitten hand is largely healed. He was unexpectedly tractable in following my instructions for care, and the result has been a smooth and speedy recovery.

The first case of scurvy has been placed on the sick list, attended with great debility; others may soon follow, although I suspect the sufferer (Milner) is unusually susceptible, for our ration of lime, though low, has not yet run dry. I have doubled his allowance, and expect him to recover at least partially. From this time, it is likely that the disease will become more generally manifest, associated with debility and rheumatism in various forms.

The men handle the extreme conditions with surprising ease and there have been fewer cases of frostbite than I anticipated, and no fights or other signs of snow madness. I observe that several men have formed certain understandings between themselves. Despite formal naval prohibitions, I see no harm in it, nor apparently does the captain, as long as it does not disrupt the harmonious running of the ship. "This is a private enterprise," is all he will say – and so it is. Indeed, in these frigid days and worse nights, one cannot begrudge anyone a modicum of human warmth.

⁂ ⁂ ⁂ ⁂ ⁂

Innugati addresses the women of Kangiqtugaapik

The qallunaat have no women. Sisters, answer me: why do they have no women? Why do they have no children? They say their women and children are in a far-off land, over the ice and the sea, so many days' journey that no Inuit have ever been there. Are there places no Inuit has ever gone? Sisters, answer me: can this be so?

Men without women are not men. Tukisiviit? They are forsaken by Pukkeenegak. They are something bad, something dangerous.

If they have never had women, never made children, they are not human. If there were women, but now they are gone – what has happened to them? Sisters, answer me: what can have happened to them?

⁂ ⁂ ⁂ ⁂ ⁂

Ship's Log
21 December 1850

The winter solstice, at last. One half of the season of darkness has passed, and we can now look forward to the return of the sun. These days of darkness are very strange and feel only half-real.

* * * * *

Ship's Log
25 December 1850

We cheerfully welcome Christmas Day, even in this most inhospitable location, and make our best efforts to mark it with as much enjoyment as circumstances, and our own resources, can admit of. The men lit up the ship with candles and lanterns, and arranged the mess tables in a long line, that they might all sit together and sing songs, and tell stories of past years. They were made merrier by several bottles of excellent whiskey provided by the first mate as a Christmas gift to the crew. Smith ransacked the larders for the choicest morsels; and, amongst the rarities produced, were beef six months old, which has been nearly all that period frozen, and a sirloin of musk ox, which would have ornamented any table in a more temperate clime. He had stowed two large puddings aboard, as well, and so our meal ended in a most suitable fashion, and we were all warmer and fuller and cheerier than we had been for many a long month.

* * * * *

Captain's Log
25 December 1850

I did not, myself, partake in the dinner, thinking that the men would prefer a celebration free from the presence of their commanding officer, but managed to swipe a bottle of Taylor's good whiskey and hide myself away beside the warm stove in the otherwise-abandoned sickbay. All told, it is not a bad way to pass an evening. I lit a candle and opened my book.

An hour or two in, and there was a rap on the door. It was Hall. Of course it was Hall, for truly there is no escape from confusion or aggravation or temptation, and life must never be simple.

"I did not see you at dinner, Captain." He looked so small in that moment, and so alone, that I held out the bottle as an offering of peace. I have no wish to hurt the man; my atrocious temper is no fault of his, nor are the thoughts in my corrupt mind.

He looked surprised, but came and sat beside me.

"Go on," I said, and he raised the bottle. I have never seen him drink before.

We sat in silence and passed the bottle between us, and the whole time I wrestled with myself. When I looked at him, his cheeks were lovely and pink, and his eyes were closed as he again tipped the bottle to his lips. It has been so long.

I am reprehensible, and I know it. Drunk and reckless and stupid. I have no business involving anyone else in my ruinous life. But still his eyes were closed and he was so beautiful, creamy skin and tangled, red curls, and – I forgot myself.

I leaned forward and pressed my mouth to his. *God*! For a moment it was –

I shall never forget how his eyes flew open. He reared back in such alarm; all I saw in his eyes was shock.

I have read all through the lens of my own sick desire, and I have been so wrong.

I muttered some apology and rose; he tried to stand, and staggered back drunkenly – Christ, he was nearly insensible with drink, and I had almost – He could hardly focus his eyes.

He was reaching for me, then, trying to speak, but I thrust him back down and went to the passageway to call for Taylor, who came over from the mess laughing and happy, and was easily prevailed upon to get the "over-merry Hall" to his bunk.

Thank God for Taylor. I know, I *know* that I am not a good man, but he unquestioningly assumes the best in me and reminds me that I can still strive to be better. I must be better than this.

⁂

Naturalist's Log
26 December 1850

God damn me for a fool. Worse than a fool. Ah, my head aches so; I cannot think! This is why I do not drink.

Why will the man not *talk* to me? My mind is all a muddle. He cannot – So good a man. He cannot have… What did he – ?

⁂

Ship's Log
31 December 1850

The weather throughout the entire of this dark and frigid December have ranged from 3° to 39° below zero, with a mean of 23° 36', that of the lower deck 48° 4', and the force of wind 2.48.

The last hours of this eventful year close on us, presenting a picture of wildness it is difficult to conceive. A heavy, northwesterly gale and dense snow-drift confine us to the ship; and thankful are we for such comfortable shelter from the pitiless blast that sweeps over us – to which we could not for an instant expose ourselves with safety.

* * * * *

Inuit saying, often repeated:

The only thing we know with any certainty is that whatever is meant to happen will happen.

Chapter Five: January – April 1851

Naturalist's Log
4 January 1851

He will not speak to me, or be alone with me, and when I knock at his door late at night, as I used to do, he does not answer.

⁂

Surgeon's Log
6 January 1851

The good captain and our intrepid naturalist are on the outs again, and more fool them. One day they are inseparable, each looking at the other as if he'd hung the moon, and the next they won't so much as speak a civil word to each other. Lord only knows what goes on between them, but any idiot can see they are quite miserable. I'm tempted to exercise my medical authority and knock their heads together.

⁂

Captain's Log
7 January 1851

Is it not enough to ensure his survival? Is it not enough to lead a crew of thirty men through fearful and extreme conditions? Must I also endure his imploring and reproachful gaze? Must I be tormented by ghosts and living spectres both?

I fear what I might do, left alone with the man. I know better, now, than to trust myself. For – and this is surely the most base aspect of my confession – I cannot regret any of my actions, and given similar circumstances, I would still do the same. And I need him. For success in this mission, I need his skill and his knowledge to guide me. I cannot risk the lives of so many who may be depending upon us.

✲ ✲ ✲ ✲ ✲

Naturalist's Log
11 January 1851

I look out for the ravens every day, and most days I espy them. In the past I would have scoffed, but that was before I had experienced the endless night of the frozen north. One begins to feel that all life is unnatural here; that the ice and snow reign supreme and will inevitably conquer all. But the ravens have learned, over countless years, countless generations, how to bear the yoke of life regardless of circumstance. Admirable creatures.

In the dark, I have dispensed with the concept of night and day. Many of the men have begun to sleep rather more than they ought, but I find the opposite: I am able to continue with my work without the unnecessary interruptions which so plague me in England. After all, it is the work that matters – that is why I am here.

✲ ✲ ✲ ✲ ✲

Ship's Log
13 January 1851

This evening, when all was still about the ship, a large bear was observed slowly coming up from the south, and stopped at about 180 yards; at this distance, he took up a position, gazing intently on the ship, and eagerly sniffing the air. We waited for a few minutes in hope of his approaching nearer; but possibly suspecting our intentions, he proceeded on his course. One of us fired and, it was thought, wounded him, as he fell on his knees, and staggered a little. He again started at a brisk pace, pursued by Taylor and a few others. Warde, our quartermaster, fired and wounded him in the hind-quarters without arresting his progress. Not having time to reload, Warde pursued him with the bayonet, having taken the precaution of fixing one to his gun in the event of coming to close quarters; but, after a fruitless chase, the bear eventually disappeared into the snow. He was a noble-looking animal, the largest we have yet seen; and we consequently regretted his escape.

✲ ✲ ✲ ✲ ✲

Ship's Log
18 January 1851

Yesterday, the first reindeer fell to our guns. It weighed sixty-seven pounds, but in its poor condition contrasted in a marked degree with those shot at the commencement of winter, as there was scarcely a vestige of fat anywhere to be seen. Today, the second fell, in the same condition as the first, and affording us a total of one hundred and two pounds of meat. Hunting is now our only sport and entertainment, and it is pursued with vigour by many of the men.

✲ ✲ ✲ ✲ ✲

20 January, 1851

TO: Abiah Higginbotham
President, Women's Suffrage Committee
37 Upper Hannover Street
Sheffield

Dear Abiah,

The final wording of the petition to the House of Lords is at last, at long, *long* last, settled amongst the membership. I may now confidently state that since this ridiculous process has not caused me to tender my resignation as Secretary, nothing at all can have that power. I know you will say that if we claim to speak for all the women of Britain, we must diligently canvas and reflect their opinions, but my dear, really, even you must admit this has been excessive.

In any case, it is finished. You may raise no further objections, nor queries, and if there is a spelling error or bit of punctuation anywhere out of place I shall hang myself immediately.

Yours,

Addie

Mrs. Addie Maxwell
Secretary, Women's Suffrage Committee
23 Little Eastcheap Street
London

Enclosure:

THE PETITION OF the Women's Suffrage Committee
Presented to Lord Howard of Essex
For submission to the House of Lords
Session 1851A

We, the petitioners of the Women's Suffrage Committee, on behalf of all the women of Britain, assert that:

1. *Under whatever conditions, and within whatever limits, men are admitted to the suffrage, there is not a shadow of justification for not admitting women under the same.*
2. *The legal subordination of one sex to another is wrong in itself, and now one of the chief hindrances to human improvement; and that it ought to be replaced by a system of perfect equality, admitting no power and privilege on the one side, nor disability on the other.*

Signatories appended numbering in excess of 1,500.

⁂⁂⁂⁂⁂

Ship's Log
2 February 1851

No day comes without seeing some of us on the hills – at least, when the conditions are such that we can possibly venture out – and no week passes without some addition being made to our stock. This is as good for crew morale as it is for our provisions, and this is a dangerous season for both. Smith and Carruthers are pleased.

⁂⁂⁂⁂⁂

Naturalist's Log
4 February 1851

The entire of the past month was remarkable for its cold, boisterous character; there were but few days that the wind did not blow with the force of a gale. The southwest and northwest winds prevailed; light snow fell on two occasions; the mean temperature was -47° and force of wind 3.4. I work, as best I can, on analysis of samples taken from the hunters' fresh kills, but in this cold, any progress is painful and slow. It wears on one. There is little, now, with which to stimulate my mind, which begins to circle in on itself. In the dark and cold, *I* grow dark and cold and intolerably maudlin.

Today I looked out at the usual time, and only one raven flew out over the ship. I had begun to suspect that the legend is true, and ravens *do* mate for life, but it seems I was too hasty. Not surprising.

* * * * *

Naturalist's Log
10 February 1851

Yesterday, when taking some exercise on the ice road, I discovered the wing-feathers of my missing raven friend, who has, no doubt, become the prey of a fox. And so I cannot draw any conclusion, for only death separated this pair. What do they do when their mate dies? Will my friend find a new mate, or is he now alone in the world? What I would not give for my library.

* * * * *

Told by Yura the beautiful at Kugluktuk in the dark season

There was a raven who wanted to marry two beautiful geese. They protested, saying that he would not be able to keep up with them on their long flights across the ocean, but he was persistent and the geese finally agreed to the marriage. On their next migration, the devoted raven accompanied the two geese. After a few hours of flying, however, he grew tired. The geese rested on the water, but since the raven was unable to swim, he begged the geese to support him between their wings. The geese carried him along good-naturedly for a while, but soon grew exhausted under his weight. Suddenly they let go of his body, and he plunged headlong into the sea and was drowned. There he was transformed into a little black mollusk which flaps along underwater and is known as tulugarnaq, the little sea raven who reflects his sky brothers.

Sisters and brothers, you think the dark will last forever, but I have chewed off part of it. Who else will take a bite?

⁂ ⁂ ⁂ ⁂ ⁂

Captain's Log
11 February 1851

A strange restlessness has begun to infect the crew – an inevitable consequence, I believe, of living so long in the cold and dark. It is not natural for men to endure such monotony. Today, I brought out my copy of Mr. Dickens' latest, and Thompson, the gunner, began to read aloud from the beginning. Most of us have already read the first chapters, but it was well to hear it again:

> *Whether I shall turn out to be the hero of my own life, or whether that station will be held by anybody else, these pages must show. To begin my life with the beginning of my life, I record that I was born (as I have been informed and believe) on a Friday, at twelve o'clock at night. It was remarked that the clock began to strike, and I began to cry, simultaneously...*

For almost two hours, the men were rapt. We shall continue with daily readings.

⁂ ⁂ ⁂ ⁂ ⁂

Surgeon's Log
14 February 1851

As the winter progresses, tension builds aboard ship. I had anticipated the cold and dark would have a soporific effect upon the men, and indeed it does, for some. For others, however, the dull boredom of the days begins to eat at them, and they grow wild with it. I send these out on the ice as often as is practicable, ostensibly to hunt but really to work off their energies in a productive fashion.

The captain maintains careful discipline aboard ship, requiring absolute obedience of action while allowing for healthy freedom of mind. I cannot discern whether he himself grows sleepy or wild, but he spends much time alone, endlessly pacing in his cabin. His eyes, when he emerges, are haunted.

I am, myself, ever more drowsy in the strange darkness of our half-life.

✲ ✲ ✲ ✲ ✲

Naturalist's Log
16 February 1851

Strong northerly winds, with a hazy atmosphere and light snow; the temperature today rose to 27 degrees below zero, and the barometers fell lower than we have previously known them – entirely at variance with the influence usually exercised by these winds. Life is utterly devoid of interest.

✲ ✲ ✲ ✲ ✲

Captain's Log
17 February 1851

Today Kennedy discovered an old *Blackwood's* that somehow found its way into our stores; felicitous discovery, for we have pored over all our books and magazines again and again, until we have nearly memorized them all.

Kennedy found an interesting bit of history, and read it aloud to the men in mess. Hall was not there – for Hall is *never* there – but it made me think of him. How interesting he would find it! I must commit it to memory, although I cannot say when I might have the opportunity to relay it.

The building of a ship to navigate beneath the surface of the sea dates back not much less than 300 years, to a time when the practical realization of the idea might seem impossible. For how to build such a ship out of timber? And how to propel it? Again, how to dwell within it when death from suffocation must so very soon put an end to the voyage? It might appear as if there were no escape from these difficulties. And yet, in spite of all, the idea was made a reality by the genius of one forgotten man.

Cornelius Drebbel is credited with actually making and working a submarine early in the seventeenth century. Drebbel was taken into favour by William the First and given residence in return for the many inventions presented to the King by the young man, and Drebbel enjoyed among his contemporaries a wide reputation for scientific attainments.

The precise date of Drebbel's invention of a submarine boat is not forthcoming from surviving references to the subject. But we appear safe in concluding that it was between the years 1612 and 1623. We know little about the details of Drebbel's submarine boat, but it is recorded that, in the boat, one could row and navigate under water from Westminster to Greenwich, the distance of two miles. In the boat, a person could see under the surface of the water.

I should dearly love to see what Hall would make of this information, and what application he could make of it in the Arctic.

* * * * *

Naturalist's Log
23 February 1851

I sink. The feeling is not unfamiliar, not unexpected.

I have a small reserve of my old vice: insurance against the very worst days. I think on it more than I should. I fear to use it, though, for once that is gone, there shall be no relief at all for me from the tortures of my own mind.

✲ ✲ ✲ ✲ ✲

Told by Nuniq, who thinks deeply, at Kugluktuk in the dark season

Lumak, a blind boy, lived with his mother and sister and their dog, Ukirk. One day, a polar bear appeared outside the window of their iglu. Lumak's mother handed the boy an arrow and led him to the window (which was now a hole as the ice pane had fallen out) and told him to kill the bear. Lumak shot the bear with his arrow. The bear let out a growl before wandering off to die. The mother had many strange and cruel ideas in her head. She turned to Lumak and said, "You have killed Ukirk, you killed the dog." But Lumak knew he had killed the bear because he had heard it growl. The mother and sister left Lumak in the iglu and went to build a new iglu closer to where the bear had died. The mother sent the sister back with a bit of meat for Lumak but told her to say that it was dog meat. When Lumak ate the meat, he knew it was polar bear meat, but he said nothing. Every few days the sister brought meat for Lumak, and each time the mother said to tell him it was dog meat.

As time passed, the old iglu began to collapse around Lumak where he sat alone and hungry. One day a loon appeared and asked Lumak to come with him to the water. Lumak followed the loon, and at the water it told him to hold onto him and not to let go. Lumak did as the loon asked. The loon dove down into the water and swam for a long time. Just when Lumak was out of air, the loon surfaced. The loon proceeded to dive down two more times, surfacing only when Lumak was out of air. When they surfaced after a third time, Lumak had regained his sight.

When Lumak returned to where his mother and sister lived, he pretended that he was still blind. He suggested that if his mother helped, he could catch a whale. When they got to the shore, Lumak prepared his harpoon and his line. He told his mother to tie the line around her waist so that when he harpooned a whale, she could help pull it in. She did as he asked. Even though Lumak's mother kept yelling at Lumak each time she saw a small whale, Lumak waited. Finally, when Lumak saw a large whale, he shot his harpoon with all his might. But rather than help his mother pull the line, Lumak stood back and let the whale pull her into the sea. This is the end of the story.

Sisters and brothers, you think the dark will last forever, but I have chewed off part of it. Who else will take a bite?

✲ ✲ ✲ ✲ ✲

Captain's Log
28 February 1851

The endless night has turned to merely a *nearly*-endless night, with heady glimpses of the beginnings of dawn. The sun has not yet made an appearance, but each day she toys with us, and each day we see more of her blush at the edges of the sky. The smallest glimmer of light – how it kindles something in the blood! How it moves one. The old Arctic hands shrug and return to their card games, while we novices pace the deck with nervous avidity.

The reading of *David Copperfield* has progressed, and we are all engrossed in the last volume that was issued before we departed England. It is an excellent reminder it is of the civilization we left behind us when we quit that country.

Much entertainment is now to be had in imagining the events of the novel to come. It is generally felt that Mr. Dickens would not end the novel on a wholly desolate note, but would allow for some measure of goodness and hope to manifest. The good Angel will surely triumph. As for myself, I cannot say. Dickens' fidelity to life is such that I cannot expect a happy ending.

✲ ✲ ✲ ✲ ✲

1 March 1851

TO: Mrs. Addie Maxwell
Secretary, Women's Suffrage Committee
23 Little Eastcheap Street
London

My dear girl,

You really must learn to master your temper if you expect to make any political progress on this or any other issue. Letters like your last will do you and your organization more harm than good, and I have thrown it in the fire for both of our sakes.

What on Earth did you expect? As I have explained to you several times, I can but present a petition to the House – I cannot compel the House to accept it. And then, even if they had accepted it, what outcome did you expect? Revolution? Overnight? I did not think you to be so naive.

My dear, Britain shall not be changed in a day, or even in a decade. *Patience* is what is required, patience and an unwavering belief in the small, incremental changes that shall one day culminate in true universal suffrage. *That* is the way our country works. Your anger and impatience only push your cause to the fringes of acceptable society – and that is very poor strategy indeed.

Please believe that I wish you all success in your future endeavours.

Sincerely,

Lord Howard of Essex
Parliament Square
London SW1

⁂ ⁂ ⁂ ⁂ ⁂

Surgeon's Log
2 March 1851

In my monthly inspection of the crew, I have observed, for the first time, a loss of flesh and strength in some; a result I was fully prepared to expect, after being four months on a reduced allowance of food, and subject to the rigour of the coldest part of the year. This is a dangerous time, as ostensibly healthy men, when weakened by circumstance, may fall prey to pneumonia, underlying tubercular tendencies, and coronary irregularities. I must be vigorous in my surveillance, and keep particular attention on Sugden, Hulott, Stone, and May. Harry Sykes is well enough; I give the boy extra rations, for he is young and growing. Current sick list appended.

I am concerned for Mr. Hall, who rarely takes his rations and appears more gaunt and pale than ever. He claims to be fully occupied in his work, but when I ask has no new findings to tell me. He always took great pleasure in demonstrating my ignorance, previously.

⁂ ⁂ ⁂ ⁂ ⁂

Told by Qimmiabruk, the little dog, at Kugluktuk in the dark season:

There was once a man who had a giant dog; it could swim in the sea, and was so big that it could drag whales and narwhals to land. The man who owned it cut holes in its jaws and fastened thongs to the holes, so he could sit on his back and ride it, and pull at these thongs when he wanted it to turn. The man had long wished for a son, but as he could not get one, he gave his dog the amulet that the child should have had. It was a knot of wood from a tree, and it was to make the dog hard against death.

Then one day the dog ate a person, so the man had to go away and settle down elsewhere. One day while he was living in that place, a kayak came in sight a long way off, and the man had to make haste and hide his dog, so that it should not eat the stranger. He led it a long way up in the hills, and gave it a large bone that it could gnaw and amuse itself with. But the dog smelt the stranger and came down from the hills, and its master then had to hide the man and his kayak far away, so that the dog should not tear them to pieces; so dangerous was it.

Though the master took great pains to hide the dog, nonetheless it made many enemies, and one day there came a strange man in a sledge with three dogs as large as bears to kill the giant dog. The man went to meet the sledge with the dog after him. At first the dog pretended to be afraid, and only when the strange dogs lunged for it did it fling itself upon them and bite through the skulls of all three.

Eventually the man noticed that the giant dog used to disappear on long excursions inland, and sometimes it came back with the leg of an inland-dweller. Then he understood that it attacked the inland-dwellers, and brought its master their legs.

From this giant dog dates the great terror that the inland-dwellers have of dogs. It always used to show itself suddenly in the opening of the window and haul them out. But it was a very good thing for the inland-dwellers to get a little fright sometimes, for they were themselves very much given to carrying off people who were alone, especially women who had lost their way in the fog.

Sisters and brothers, you think the dark will last forever, but I have chewed off part of it. Who else will take a bite?

⁂ ⁂ ⁂ ⁂ ⁂

Surgeon's Log
9 March 1851

Our little expedition has no chaplain, but on Sundays, our very devout mate Robert Wynniatt holds small services, simple Bible readings and a hymn or two. Most men do not attend, but during the darkness, more have been drawn. It is a way to mark and pass time, if nothing else. I go myself, as it is helpful in keeping to some kind of regular schedule. Today's reading was from Second Peter; exceptionally appropriate in this time of not-quite-dark and not-quite-light, and a helpful reminder for us all.

> *Add to your faith virtue; and to virtue knowledge; and to knowledge temperance; and to temperance patience; and to patience godliness; and to godliness brotherly kindness; and to brotherly kindness charity. For if these things be in you, and abound, they make you that ye shall neither be barren nor unfruitful in the knowledge of our Lord Jesus Christ. But he that lacketh these things is blind, and cannot see afar off, and hath forgotten that he was purged from his old sins. Wherefore the rather, brethren, give diligence to make your calling and election sure: for if ye do these things, ye shall never fall, for so an entrance shall be ministered unto you abundantly into the everlasting kingdom of our Lord and Saviour Jesus Christ.*

⁂ ⁂ ⁂ ⁂ ⁂

Captain's Log
9 March 1851

"Add to your faith virtue," the Good Book counsels. And if one has no faith? I often suspect that virtue is nothing more than the effective masking of the beast that sleeps within us all.

✲ ✲ ✲ ✲ ✲

Told by Uki, the survivor, at Kugluktuk in the dark season:

Remember the story of the moon and the sun: the man who lay with his sister. What I have heard is that the brother became the moon and the sister became the sun. One year, the sister did not attend the qaggiq with the rest of the people. She stayed at her own hearth, and whenever she was all alone someone would rush in and blow out the flames so it became dark, and a man would lie with her at that moment. She never found out who it was, so when he did it again she covered her hand in soot and made a mark on the man. When he finished she followed him back to the qaggiq. When the man entered, she saw in the light that it was her brother. At once she went into the qaggiq and, taking up the great hunting knife, cut off her breast and offered it to her brother saying: "if you would take me, take all of me. If one part of me is worthy, *all* of me is worthy." Of course the brother did not eat what was offered to him by his sister. He scooped up some of the fire with an ulu and ran out-doors; his sister likewise scooped up a flame and ran after him, her breast in her hand, outstretched in fierce offering. They started to go round and round the qaggiq with the sister ahead of the brother with a flame in hand. The flame from the brother went out so that it was now only smolder, while the flames on the sister kept burning; so this was the way she became the sun while the brother became the moon.

Sisters and brothers, you think the dark will last forever, but I have chewed off part of it. Who else will take a bite?

✲ ✲ ✲ ✲ ✲

10 March 1851

TO: Abiah Higginbotham
President, Women's Suffrage Committee
37 Upper Hannover Street
Sheffield

Abiah,

I enclose my recent, most detestable letter from Lord Howard for your perusal. *Damn* the man! Does he imagine we are unaware of the way this country functions? We work and we work, and in the end, nothing changes. Or perhaps it does, but deathly slowly, and Abiah, I cannot endure it. He bids us to wait and calls me his "dear." *Wait.* I cannot wait for men to decide my fate! Not any longer. And yet, what choice have I – have we?

I strive to tell myself stories in these dark times, stories to deploy against despair: perseverance in the face of injustice, victory against insurmountable odds. And all that comes to mind is Clarissa Harlowe, or Tess of the D'Urbervilles, or Cathy Earnshaw. Stories of women punished for the supreme crime of acting as though they are fully human. Stories of men who would gladly take our bodies and steal our labour, men who would consume us, and leave aside the parts that are not palatable or beneficial to them, not knowing (or not caring!) that such a division is nothing less than spiritual *death* for us.

I do not accept the need for change to be incremental. I do not accept this fate for our daughters, and I do not accept it for ourselves.

I am sorry that my letter is so bilious, but I cannot find it in me to smile now, to be the good angel Lord Howard expects. I feel sometimes that I will strangle on my own bitterness. I can scarcely breathe.

I do not know what to do.

Most sincerely,

Addie

✲ ✲ ✲ ✲ ✲

14 March 1851

TO: Mrs. Addie Maxwell
Secretary: Women's Suffrage Committee
23 Little Eastcheap Street
London

My dear, dear Addie.

I have sat over this letter for several long hours, and written many pages which I have then destroyed. To begin: you must not doubt that I am as bitterly disappointed by the rejection of the petition as you are – disappointed and furious and despairing. And yet, in a day or two, or perhaps a week, I know that I shall dry my tears and begin the work again. But Addie, I fear for you. You are not made for incremental campaigns such as ours. You are not patient. You are the ever-moving ocean, not the staid and placid shore, and I fear you will do yourself harm in throwing yourself ceaselessly against the uncaring rocks. I love you far too well to allow this.

Addie, you must be cautious. What good will you be to the movement if you do not take care to maintain your equilibrium? We do not want a broken foot soldier – and I do not want a broken friend. I have seen it happen too many times, my dear. Do not allow it to happen to you. Do not permit yourself to break.

I have thought and thought on what to advise you, and I believe I have hit upon an idea. Terrible doctors are always prescribing "changes of air," are they not? Why not go away for a month or two? The country, or even the continent? Spend some time in absolute pleasure and self-indulgence, and do not think of this sad business for the entire time you are away. The Committee can hobble along without you for a little while. The work will still be here for you when you return, and you will be in a better frame of mind to bear it.

Please, Addie, do consider it.

I wish you
All my love,

Abiah Higginbotham
President, Women's Suffrage Committee
37 Upper Hannover Street
Sheffield

✲ ✲ ✲ ✲ ✲

Ship's Log
26 March 1851

And so has disaster struck. Not the event so long dreaded: all is well with the ship, and we have no news of Cauderson – but a new disaster, more terrible for being so stupidly unforeseen and eminently preventable. Naturalist Hall has gone missing from the ship. It is surmised that he has undertaken a grievously misjudged expedition, telling no one aboard, and that he has lost his way or some other disaster has befallen him, rendering him somehow incapable of returning. We have reason to believe he is not well.

We have taken inventory of his quarters, and ascertained that his cold-weather garb is gone. We know, then, that he is at least minimally dressed for the conditions.

He has been absent seven hours, and we are much alarmed. Immediately upon discovery of his absence, a mortar was fired, and rockets subsequently, at quarter-hour intervals, but without any apparent recognition. We now prepare three search parties, each supplied with rockets, blue lights, emergency tents, and refreshments, to prosecute the search in different directions.

✲ ✲ ✲ ✲ ✲

Captain's Log
26 March 1851

Damn the man!

Please, God. Let him live. I shall never forgive myself if –

✲ ✲ ✲ ✲ ✲

Ship's Log
28 March 1851

At the first glimmer of dawn on the morning of the 27th, our three searchers were dispatched from the ship, fanning out in three directions. Leaving Taylor in command in my absence, I took it upon myself to join the active search, along with volunteers Wynniatt and Lucas. It was several hours of hard hiking before I came upon the unfortunate object of our search. It appeared that the man had wanted some geological samples for his experiments, and most ill-advisedly made off into the howling night without informing anyone. He walked for some time, when, growing cold, he found himself unable to regain the ship, having, in his eagerness, paid no attention to the direction he was going in. He wandered about in vain seeking his homeward route, when, luckily, I came across his path. He seemed to be in a half demented state, overcome by fatigue and cold. It took several hours in a make-shift tent for me to warm and revive him to the point that he would agree to continue on with me to the ship. At last, he was persuaded to walk a little; but soon sunk in the snow in a state of utter helplessness, with haemorrage from mouth and nose, and partially convulsed. I saw that the poor fellow must soon expire, if a vigorous effort was not made to relieve him; yet our distance from the skip precluded the possibility of seeking assistance – before I could reach the ship, the man would be frozen to death, and a prey to the wolves then heard howling in the distance.

One alternative alone remained, and that was promptly adopted. Carry him I could not, as I am about the slightest, and he one of the tallest in the ship; nor would my small provision sled suffice to bear him across the ice. So, slinging my gun over my shoulder, I abandoned the sled and, with the man's arms around my neck, I commenced the task of dragging him over the snow in the direction of the ship. This had the good effect of exciting the vital powers, and antagonizing in some degree, the lethargic sleep of death rapidly stealing over us both. What took me three hours to walk singly took more than double that time with my charge, and when we reached within a mile of the ship, I found my own physical powers giving way. Having succeeded in arousing a little more life in the helpless man, I laid him in a bed of snow, and started off for assistance, firing my gun to draw the attention of the distant crew. As the night was intensely cold, with a fresh breeze, and a temperature of 57° below freezing point, I knew the tragic scene must soon come to an end if relief did not speedily reach him.

I was met at about 22:30, about three quarters of a mile from the ship, and we returned to Hall and dragged him between the four of us back to the ship. He was in a state of insensibility, arms and legs stiff and rigid – the former extended, could with difficulty be bent – hands clenched and frozen, eyes fixed and glassy, jaws rigid and both so firmly clenched that we could scarcely separate them to pour down restoratives. The pulse was imperceptible at the wrist, the heart barely acting. All being in readiness for his reception, the work of resuscitation commenced, which I had the satisfaction of seeing attended with success. Reactionary fever with delirium ensued, but from these, Carruthers assures me he will recover.

Captain's commendations for Wynniatt, Lucas, and Carruthers.

* * * * *

Captain's Log
30 March 1851

The past several days have been some of the most difficult I have endured. I have now, at least, recovered enough to make some private record of the whole misadventure.

I shall begin at the beginning of the whole painful affair.

In this private record, I can explain that certain men – men of specific tastes and habits – have certain ways of telegraphing certain proclivities to certain other men. Our Able Seaman Johnny Griggs, for example, has made himself clear to me from almost the instant of our first meeting. He is an appealing man, and I have been tempted, but too I have been preoccupied, and – well. It has not suited me to accept his repeated offers. This season, though, is so very dark, and I so long alone – it has been tempting. And the relentless hours of vacant time! One is so bored, then insipid and dull, then slowly one grows restless, and then desperate for – one knows not what.

Two nights ago, Griggs again offered. I accepted – I should not have, but I longed to feel warm, human flesh against me, and I am weak, and so I did. He came to my great cabin, well past midnight when the ship was quiet and only the watch on deck still awake.

We were, I realize now, not discreet. I inexcusably failed to bolt the door, and he inexcusably failed to shut his damned pretty mouth when things grew heated between us.

To cut a sordid scene short: Hall burst through the door, a concerned inquiry on his lips, and found me fucking Griggs most enthusiastically over the table in my private cabin.

I imagined I had seen shock and alarm on his face before this – it was as nothing to this. The man looked as if he had been physically struck, his mouth gaping wide and his eyes – pained. "Excuse me," he muttered. "I was mistaken." And he withdrew, shutting the door behind him.

I pushed Griggs aside – rather more roughly than I should have. I could not continue with him. I could not *look* at him.

He muttered a curse under his breath, and when I looked again, he was gone.

I did not look in again on Hall until the next morning, but lay wrestling with myself in the dark silence. I was angry – very angry – but I could not say why, or with whom.

I rose when the ship's bell rang out the hour of 06:00 and knocked at Hall's door. I could not even have said what I hoped to accomplish by speaking to him – just that I felt the overwhelming need to somehow clear the air between us.

But only silence answered my rap. His cabin was empty, his belongings in disarray. On his bed, quite in the open, sat a hypodermic syringe and an empty phial. For a moment, my anger overtook me, and I was obliged to pause and master myself. Finally, I secreted the incriminating objects in my pocket, and then called for Carruthers and Taylor. We searched the ship from top to bottom as thoroughly and discreetly as we could: I almost blind with rage.

I ripped apart his cabin, seeking some clue as to where the man could have gone, and evidence of any other substance he could use to do himself harm. I found nothing at all. He had held that single dose on reserve, and last night – he had needed it.

I was mystified by this, for no explanation seemed to fit into my own understanding of the man and his character, but I hardly had time to think of that in the urgency of the situation: if Hall was on the ice, he would not survive for long.

We then began the search in earnest – Taylor outfitting three sleds for search parties, I ordering the guns to be fired and every light aboard ship to be lit.

I have had occasion before to bless Taylor and to thank Providence for his service, and I certainly did again. He was quick, efficient, and discreet in all his doings, and he did not question my determination to be part of the active search.

"Good luck sir," he said, as I pulled on my cold-weather slops. "Hall is the cleverest bastard I've ever met. If anyone can survive, he can."

I nodded. "No man of mine will perish on this mission if I can help it," I replied, but the wind howled with such viciousness that my heart misgave me.

Wynniatt, Lucas, and I each took our little sleds and tethered them around our shoulders. The wind had polished the snow to such a glossy hardness that it was almost easy to pull. We fanned out from the ship, equidistant from each other, in order to sweep the area as efficiently and thoroughly as possible. Wynniatt flanked me to the left, and Lucas to the right. It was too dim, and the wind too strong, to hope for tracks, and indeed there were none.

Within minutes, we were out of sight of each other, the wind howling with such violence that even calling out was fruitless. The light and intermittent signals from the ship allowed us to orient ourselves, and so stay on our planned paths.

In the half-light of the Arctic day, with snow and wind swirling constantly around me, it became impossible to keep track of time. It felt like days before I stumbled across the figure lying in the snow – and it was only luck that I found him at all, for had I passed a dozen yards to either side of him, I would never have seen him.

He was only partially conscious when I found him, covered with a thin layer of snow, numb and stupid with cold. I knew I would have to warm him before attempting to transport him back to the ship, for he would not likely survive another long journey in such temperatures. I took the canvas frame from my sled and pitched a make-shift tent around him where he lay, pulling him up onto a buffalo hide blanket and sealing the canvas around him as best I could. Then I crawled in as well, half beside and half on top of him in the tiny space. My body heat would help warm the air around him, and perhaps he would revive more quickly.

He was murmuring to himself all the time that I worked, incoherent mutterings and strange, aborted, half-stumbling gestures that were impossible to interpret. I could not judge whether his condition was a result of the cold, or of the cocaine he had taken.

I lit our tiny spirit heater – again, thank God for Taylor's foresight – our only external source of warmth, and within minutes the small space of the tent began to warm, slightly.

I became aware, suddenly, that Hall had ceased his muttering, and shook him roughly in alarm.

"Hall! Embleton! Wake up! Don't dare fall asleep. Speak to me."

His eyes cracked open, and he regarded me stupidly.

"Speak to me," I repeated.

He said nothing, but his eyes remained open, and his breath, though quick and shallow, was regular.

After twenty or thirty minutes of this, he began to shake, which I took as an excellent sign that his hypothermia was abating. I began to chafe his extremities, hoping to prevent frostbite as much as possible.

Gradually, his chattering began to form syllables, then words, then almost-intelligible strings of words. The pupils of his eyes were like tiny pinpricks, and his body was wracked with convulsive shudders, but I was able to make out some of what he said.

"D– D– David. You have no right – no right, David! – to make me feel things – such things as I do not –" He broke off into a convulsive shiver. "I am an *abhorrent* man, D– David. I thought m – my nature would repel you… I did not imagine –"

I longed to hush him, to question him, to – to embrace him in his misery. We were so close in the tiny make-shift tent.

I am a coward, and I did nothing.

"You do not want me, but –" he took a deep, shuddering breath. "To take just any –. Anyone at all to your b– To your bed. *Griggs?* Without an ounce of interest about him! S– Such a man as that? I do not understand. It is in– insupportable."

I shook my head at that. He was half dead from cold and influenced by cocaine. He did not know what he was saying, and anyway – I could not explain myself. Suddenly, my anger came roaring back.

"Insupportable?" I hissed. "And I suppose it is *supportable* to drug oneself into oblivion? To abscond from a place of safety to one of mortal danger? I suppose it is supportable to, through insane self-slaughter, most selfishly deny the world of an exceptional naturalist? To deny me of – of my true friend? Is that *supportable*?"

He blinked at me owlishly and did not reply. I do not know that he comprehended a word I said, for the next instant, his eyes rolled up and his head lolled frighteningly to the side.

All the fight left me. I grabbed him and shook him, slapping his face and shouting his name in panic. And then I remembered my flask, and fumblingly tipped a good dose of brandy up into his mouth.

He spluttered and began again to shake, but his eyes opened. He yet lived.

"Keep speaking. Please. I am sorry. Stay with me. Try to stay awake."

He laughed then, as I have never heard him laugh: a thin, reedy, most unnatural sound.

"Stay with you!" he gasped at last. "You are the most –"

He leaned back against the blanket and closed his eyes for a moment, but when they opened they fixed on me with startling intensity.

"Speak to me of Caulderson," he said at last, and his voice was low, terribly low, but clearer than it had been. His words were nothing less than a command. I leaned closer to hear him better. "You ask me to find him," he continued. "You ask me to care about him, to work for him, to help you find – I don't know – your former commander? Your friend? Your – your lover? You give me no useful information about the man, and expect me to care for him as you do? And then – You embrace me! You kiss me, David, and then you drive me away! And do not speak to me! And will not tell me why!"

By the end of this long speech, he was gasping for breath and shuddering in my arms, but I heard every word, and each landed as a lash across my back.

I could not dissemble, not in such circumstances, and yet it is so difficult to speak a heart's truth. "You wish to know about Caulderson?" I asked – for perhaps that was the least impossible of his questions. His eyes were trained on my face. "Then know all: I love him. I loved him. I loved him and I saved him, and I have been damned ever since." My face was wet and cold. "And Embleton," I continued helplessly, "understand this: I will not – I will *not* – subject you to the same fate."

He sighed then, just once, as if all his strength was gone, and leaned back again into his blanket. He shook his head once, quickly, and then lay still.

I started up in alarm, but his hand found mine, and pressed it, once. "Thank you, David," he whispered. "I must rest. Give me an hour, please."

I did, of course. It was perhaps the longest hour of my life, lying in the dark with Embleton Hall, listening for his every breath above the howling of the Arctic wind, and fearing that it would not come.

How we made it through the long trek back to the *Serapis*, I do not know. I dragged him the whole way through that nightmarish, barren landscape, the savage wind biting and tearing at us with every step. I could not stop to rest, for fear of never rising again. By the end I was staggering, my limbs entirely numb and every muscle shaking with fatigue, and he was a dead weight at my side. I did not know if he yet lived, and all I could do was carry on blindly.

It took two men to crack me out of my slops when we finally reached the ship, for the wind had driven the snow through the thick wool of my outer great coat and deep into the inner layers, where it had melted with my body heat, and then frozen again in a crackling shell.

Carruthers had Hall carried immediately to sickbay. I passed several fearful hours when Hall's fate hung in the balance, but Carruthers assures me now that his survival is certain, and that his full recovery simply requires time.

Time is the one thing we have in plentiful supply. We sit in the dark, in the cold, and put our faith in the growing fingers of dawn that light the sky – a little more each day. We put our faith in spring.

* * * * *

13 April 1851

TO: Sir Francis Hall
Ashfield Manor
Caterham on the Hill, Surrey

Sir,

I have to request that you will do me the favour of granting me the sum of £65 from the arrears of my husband's pay, or such further portion of it, as will amount to one half of the salary due to him since his departure from England.

I make the request as needing this sum for subsistence, as well as for the liquidation of some small debts, and because he authorized me to draw his pay if I required it.

I have refrained hitherto from making any regular application for this money as a legitimate part of my income, mainly from my repugnance to present such undignified repeated requests. I find, however, that I am now in dire need of it.

I have the honour to be

Sir

your obed serv

Addie Maxwell
23 Little Eastcheap Street
London

* * * * *

Naturalist's log
20 April 1851

I am too weak still to tell the story; indeed, I wish nothing more than to forget it all. Already what I remember is vague and dream-like. I remain susceptible to cold. I have no more cocaine. I am a fool. David came to see me every day in sickbay, while Carruthers was at mess. I am more compromised than ever I was, and he? He is far kinder than I deserve, and every act of kindness stings like a lash.

Chapter Six:
May – August 1851

Ship's Log
7 May 1851

The daylight lasts longer each day, and the temperature rises, though gradually. The men are slower, thinner, more ragged than they were before this difficult season, but the daylight invigorates them. We have eagerly begun to prepare the ship for spring, although we are unlikely to see the summer thaw for six more weeks, at least. It is my intention that it will find us in a state of high efficiency, ready to sail hard in pursuit of our quarry and withdraw before the ice catches us in another winter. The first task must be to ascertain the exact quantity, state and condition of the provisions on board, that we might be fully aware of the extent of our resources, a very necessary measure of precaution. The holds have been accordingly cleared out, and light and air admitted; this tended much to their purification, and then the contents were enumerated and returned. We must continue to augment our existing rations with fresh meat; if we do so, our remaining rations will last another 5 months, even given the disastrous losses we suffered in our Atlantic crossing.

* * * * *

Naturalist's Log
13 May 1851

I have begun to recommence some of my duties, being now largely recovered from what the Captain and Carruthers refer to as my "most recent misadventure." The ice increased nine inches whilst I was kept to sickbay, and is now six feet, five inches thick. I have resumed my atmospheric readings, as well as several of my more stable anatomical experiments.

I remember perhaps only a quarter of all the things that transpired on the ice, and for all the hardship, for all the humiliation, for all the suffering, I feel – scoured out.

There is a little moth, the *Gynaephora groenlandica*, samples of which I collected early on in our sojourn here (12J.6509 through 12J.6514). As a little caterpillar, it spends most of its lifespan – thought to be up to 14 years, although this is as yet unconfirmed – actually frozen in the ice in a protective hibernaculum, and pupates only when and if it reaches both maturity and necessary external temperatures with precise simultaneity. If these conditions are met? Metamorphosis! by processes unknown. Such fragile, hardy little creatures.

* * * * *

Captain's Log
14 May 1851

Carruthers came to my great cabin tonight and spoke to me at some length about the health and morale of the crew: the former which suffers now that the harsh conditions of the Arctic winter have exposed underlying weaknesses in several men's constitutions, and the latter which grows more robust as spring at last approaches. He is particularly concerned about second mate Stephen Court, who has been unable to perform even light duties for several weeks, and has been confined to sickbay for the past few days with a tubercular cough.

Carruthers further requested to conduct an examination upon my person, with particular attention to the action of the vital organs, given my recent loss of flesh.

I smiled ruefully and removed my jacket and shirt, indicating that he should begin. "I am not ill," I said, "but by all means, you must do your duty. I fear," I added unthinkingly, "that if we find Caulderson – *when* we find him – he will find me gravely changed."

Carruthers looked at me quite piercingly then; he is a man so kindly, so blandly sympathetic, that I often overlook his surprising perspicacity. He finished his examination of me, and pronounced me fit and well, if slightly undernourished. I agreed to finish my rations each day, and he seemed satisfied. Before he left, though, he put a hand on my shoulder and spoke to me seriously.

"I am addressing you now as a medical man, David, as well as your friend. I will tell you the same thing I told Hall when first he awoke after his ordeal on the ice. Men heal, and in the healing, change. Men who do not – die." He squeezed my shoulder once, then turned and left me, shouldering his way through the narrow companionway.

I have sat here thinking on his words for an hour or more. I think perhaps Carruthers is a very wise man.

* * * * *

17 May 1851

TO: Abiah Higginbotham
President, Women's Suffrage Committee
37 Upper Hannover Street
Sheffield

Dear Abiah,

I hold in my hands a rather exciting piece of paper. Shall I tell you? It is a moderately large banker's draft from one Sir Francis Hall – more than enough to allow me to take a small cottage in the country for a lengthy period. Thank heavens for my husband's most considerate arrangements for my care in his absence. And should his absence continue, I can always sell the house in Eastcheap Street. I am, at least, provided for.

I have decided to follow your excellent advice and go to the country for the foreseeable future. I wonder only why I did not think of such a course of action earlier myself. I must make a change, Abiah, you are quite right. Perhaps in the midst of fine, fresh country air, I shall be able to breathe again without the rancor that poisons me here. At any rate, I shall try.

I am considering Brighton, upon the sterling recommendation of both Mrs. Wilcox and Louisa Iverson. The seaside would be bracing, would it not? And you will come to visit? I plan to stay until – I hardly know. Until I am properly myself again.

I shall, of course, forward my address when I have secured one!

Yours in most sincere Love, Gratitude, and Admiration,

Addie

23 Little Eastcheap Street
London

* * * * *

Naturalist's Log
17 May 1851

Yesterday, during the prevalence of a south-easterly gale, the temperature rose in the course of four and twenty hours from 30° below zero to 16° above it, but today it is as low as before; a wonderful change in such a brief period, caused surely by the warmer air brought up by the gale.

There is another thawing with which I have even less first-hand experience. The captain and I have resumed our evening walks when the weather permits, striking out a mile or three on the ice road before turning back again. Often the wind makes conversation impossible, but those are somehow the best walks of all.

* * * * *

Ship's Log
25 May 1851

Many more animals have been observed by the watch since the weather began to warm, however slightly: fowl and small mammals – even a pair of caribou. Today I took a hunting party five miles inland and had far better success that we have had all winter. We returned at 23:00 with a small sledge piled high with game. On our return to the ship, we had the pleasure of seeing her dark hull again exposed to view – the deep snow embankment which concealed it having been removed during our absence by a work party led by Taylor. Thus unrobed, she presented a pleasing contrast to the white surface around. Caulder prepared a late feast of fresh, roasted meat which the men devoured avidly; they have been on three-quarters rations for many months, and relished the plentiful offerings. The remaining meat will be salted and stored for future rations.

* * * * *

Ship's Log
30 May 1851

An event of great importance in spring operations took place today: the removal of the snow from the upper deck. It was wonderful to see what an altered appearance everything presented on board. Pleasing and agreeable was it, indeed, to all the men, to walk the planks again, and to receive, between decks, the light of day from which we have been so long excluded.

* * * * *

Naturalist's Log
1 June 1851

The last of the very cold winter months have come to an end. In May, the mean temperature of 28° below zero was higher by 18° than that of the preceding month, although the range differed but little, from 6° to 51° below zero. Cold westerly and northwesterly winds generally prevailed.

During my time in sickbay, Carruthers developed a most gratifying interest in the potential medicinal properties of Arctic flora. We had many long conversations on the subject, and his questions were surprisingly insightful on several occasions. I daresay he is a man too often underestimated. In any case, I went yesterday to meet him in sickbay to clarify a point I had made about a certain species of lichen. There were murmurs in the companionway, and when I paused, I heard voices emanating from the now nearly-empty bread room. The door was slightly ajar, and from my position in the dark corridor – for I carry no lantern, as a rule – I could see the silhouettes of David – of Maxwell, and of Griggs, speaking softly with their heads together. I saw Griggs place his hand on

David's arm, and David smile and shake his head. Griggs removed his hand. They spoke for a few minutes more, and then David looked around briefly, and leaned in to kiss Griggs' cheek. Only his cheek. Griggs stepped back and tossed off a neat salute, but he, too, was smiling.

I suppose that the man will never cease to surprise me, and that I am damned to a life of – of *fundamentally not understanding*. He is not one thing. I may call myself by many names, many titles, but I am – to my core – a naturalist: I seek to know. That is my essence. David – is *not* one thing. When he says he is a husband, that he loves his wife, he does not lie. He is that, and fully. But that does not stop him from being fully a sailor, fully a commander. Fully Caulderson's lover. Fully a friend. He inhabits so many things so completely; it is quite alarming. I stood in my dark corner and watched his neat and efficient step take him back up the ladders to the main deck.

Later, he called me to his great cabin and asked me to run another test on my experimental design of gunpowder as an ice-blasting agent, as we know not how soon an opportunity will occur when gunpowder might aid our advance. I resolved to again test its efficacy, this time on a floe of last year's ice, about four feet thick and in our immediate vicinity. A hole was accordingly bored until the water was reached, and a small cask containing forty-seven pounds of powder was placed beneath the floe, and ignited by means of a Pickford's fuse. The explosion which took place eleven minutes after the fuse was ignited, caused the ejection of a cloud of broken ice and water to an elevation of eighty or one hundred feet in the air and produced an opening in the ice twenty-five feet in diameter, from whence fissures radiated in different directions from sixty to two hundred feet. This experiment may be taken as a fair instance of the effects of a given charge of gunpowder on ice of a certain character under the most favorable circumstances. The shock of the explosion was felt on board, and caused our bells to ring without a pull.

⚬ ⚬ ⚬ ⚬ ⚬

Ship's Log
13 June 1851

We are in a state of anxious preparation for the great event, to which we all ardently look forward: our release from the ice. We continue to observe the slightest movements and noises in the ice with breathless anticipation. It has decreased in thickness by two feet, two inches during the previous fortnight. A parhelion was visible this evening at 20:00, but much less brilliant than this beautiful phenomenon, as seen in the winter.

* * * * *

Ship's Log
17 June 1851

A cheering report from the ice master in the crow's nest: a space of open water has been observed extending along the eastern shore to the northward for a couple of miles, the first blue water yet seen this year. Furthermore, the visit of a few mosquitoes caused a lively degree of interest this evening, and we submitted to their assault with very different feelings than they would have created under other circumstances.

* * * * *

Surgeon's Log
21 June 1851

Court is dying of tuberculosis. There is very little I can do for him, besides keeping him comfortable; the disease must have taken hold of him long ago, and lain dormant until he was weakened by this last stretch of cold. I have informed the captain that I do not expect him to last another month. I have not attended a death in many years. I miss my colleagues, particularly in these instances in which I would normally seek out their counsel.

Our stores of lime are more than half depleted, but it is my observation – in keeping with the suspicion of many of my colleagues in London – that the lime loses its potency over time. Several men have complained of the aches and fatigue that comprise the first symptoms of scurvy, and this despite their daily ration. The course of the illness may be halted and reversed if I can harvest sufficient anti-scorbutics during the coming warm season. This shall be my first priority.

I have noticed a positive change in the health of our captain. He keeps to his word, and consumes all of his rations every day – but more than that, there is a new resolve about him that I have not seen before. He is a stubborn man, Lord knows, and it appears now that he is willing himself to be less troubled. I do not know what grievous wound afflicts him, but I believe he is beginning to heal.

* * * * *

27 June 1851

TO: Doctor Barnabas Brown
#9 Harley Street
London, West 1

Dr. Brown,

Dear sir, please come at once. Father is dreadfully ill and I can do nothing for him. He has not eaten in two days, but will not sit or rest or sleep, but only walks about in a state of continual agitation. The things he says, sir! Please, we await your coming. I know he has treated you most deplorably in the past, but please, think of me here by myself. Be merciful and come.

Yours most sincerely,

Hannah Crawley
54 Oxford Street
London

* * * * *

Ship's Log
28 June 1851

Each successive day reveals some change in the aspect of the ice; the cracks to the southward having opened out considerably and connected themselves with the water formed along either shore. We anxiously wait for each successive tide to break up those barriers by which we are still retained. We will not be kept much longer in bondage.

* * * * *

Ship's Log
2 July 1851

At an early hour, the ice was observed in motion, but until 10:30 we were still stationary as far as our landmarks enabled us to determine; then the ice under our stern became detached from the floe, and was borne a few feet to the northward, leaving the ship in a lane of water which opened out into the large expanse to the northwest. In the probability of our being separated from our well tried, trusty floe, anchors were laid out, by means of which we prevented rupture.

The anchors were not laid out too soon, but proved a good precautionary measure, for at 14:40 the ice separated and broke up so gently about us, that the first intimation we had of this great fact, was seeing the ship floating in and surrounded once more by her own element

– thus testifying that the long-wished-for period of liberation has arrived. We were slowly borne to the northwest in company with our floe, with scarcely a breath of air.

So sudden was our departure that some of our men who had gone for their washed clothes, then drying on a neighbouring floe, barely had time to regain the ship. Though we greatly rejoice at our deliverance, we cannot hope to make much westerly advance for some time, as much ice yet remains.

I therefore determined to take advantage of our small lane of open water, which extends for a short distance to the northwest, and with a fair wind to make sail, run as far as possible. For this purpose, we were at last obliged to part from our old and faithful icy friend, which had borne us in safety through so many trying scenes and perils.

Accordingly, at 16:00 we cast off from it, and the joyful pipe of "All hands make sail," was heard for the first time in many months. Right cheerfully was it responded to, and we soon saw with delight our little ship once more under canvas, making the best of her way through loose ice, backing and filling alternately, to clear numerous opposing obstacles until 19:30, when our further progress became so impeded that we were obliged to secure the ship to a large floe, and continue drifting again as before.

⁂⁂⁂⁂⁂

Medical Certificate of Cause of Death

To the Registrar General, London

I hereby certify that I attended Mr. Michael Crawley of Oxford Street, aged 62 last birthday; that I last saw him on 25 March 1851, that he died on 28 June 1851 at 3:35 a.m. and that the cause of his death was (a) first, apoplexy; complicated by (b) chronic neurasthenia. Death occurred immediately following a major apoplectic attack in presence of Miss Hannah Crawley, daughter.

I further certify that the deceased died of natural causes, and that an inquest was not required prior to burial.

Signed: Dr. Barnabas Brown
Address: #9 Harley Street, London

Certificate issued this 4th day of July in the year of our Lord 1851.

* * * * *

Ship's Log
7 July 1851

Today we at last made sail through an open space of water which led us north around Cape Dundas and into Parry Sound. We reached the edge of a large floe, into an indentation in which the ship was warped and again secured. A considerable space of open water was observed to the west, continuous with that on the south shore of which I have before spoken. It was agonizing to view such an opening without being able to reach it. And then at 16:00, our position again became so critical that a repetition of the measures necessary for a sudden abandonment of the ship was very properly adopted. The floe, on the outer edge of which we were secured, had from the effects of pressure become completely turned round, so as to place us between it and the shore, and we found ourselves distant from the latter not more than 600 yards, so that any pressure acting on its distant edge must have thrown us at once on the beach. We lay within the influence of the slightest exercise of its power. Thus threatened by ice on one hand and the shore on the other, we rejoiced when a slight change in the pressure enabled us to escape from our position and warp into one of greater safety.

The ice then began to open about us most wonderfully, which enabled us to move clear of danger, and as the water increased, the boats were lowered to tow for the first time this season. A fresh breeze soon afterwards springing up enabled us to make clear of all opposing difficulties, and at midnight we reached the long-desired open water of Parry Sound, with appearances auspicious for our northerly advance. Ship's naturalist reports the temperature of air ranged from 40° to 52°, that of water from 32° to 36°; specific gravity 1014. This change, the most sanguine amongst us could not have hoped for, much less foreseen, but such is the ever varying aspect this element assumes when once in motion, that it is impossible to predict its changes, or foretell what a few hours may bring forth.

✲ ✲ ✲ ✲ ✲

Captain's Log
26 July 1851

How well it is to be in open water again. And so early in the season – almost a month earlier than Taylor would normally expect! There remains, only, the question of our precise route. I have my instructions from Sir Francis Hall: to sail the strait between Baring Island and Prince Albert Land, into the uncharted Esquimeaux territory beyond. He made a mark on the chart to represent his prediction of where Caulderson will be found, and if all goes well, we should be able to reach that point in a fortnight or a little more.

This evening I asked Embleton Hall to my great cabin and laid my charts out on my table. We stood together looking down at them, and I said not a word – for I was curious to see whether his thoughts would match those of his father.

After several minutes of close study, he nodded decisively and took up a small pin, which he stuck in place – at precisely the same location his father had predicted over a year ago.

"There," he said. "It is impossible to account for all the potential variables, but all things being equal, we shall find the ship, the men, or at the very least, news of them, at this spot."

I thanked him very sincerely, but made no mention of our patron's opinion; I hope I am a wiser fool than that. Then again, the difference between a wise man and a fool is something with which I am increasingly unconcerned. Similarly, moral and immoral. In the end, such words matter little, and the best a man can hope is that he has been resolute in living his truth, whatever that may be. I have been giving the matter much thought.

* * * * *

Ship's Log
28 July 1851

Luck is with us; conditions have been most favourable, and we traversed Parry Sound swiftly and easily. With such progress, we can now well afford a brief hunting expedition on Baring Island, which should also please Dr. Carruthers, who seeks certain plants that grow wild and act as anti-scorbutic agents. We weighed anchor in an uncharted place we have called Serapis Bay (115°W and 73.5°N; entered into chart 1851C, appended), and rowed the jolly boat to shore with a party of five hunters, myself, the surgeon, and the naturalist.

Seals are numerous; they move about quite sluggishly, apparently free from care or strife, and equally ignorant of our rifles and the harpoon of the Esquimeaux. When we approached the shore, we were astonished to see evidence of fire, but upon investigation Hall deemed the smoke as being entirely the result of chemical action in the soil. We passed a fruitful and enjoyable day ashore. The hunters returned from their labours with so much meat as to render it necessary to take two trips back to the ship, so as to accommodate the weight of it all. Smith will be well occupied in cooking and preserving it. Among our kills are two large seals, for although their meat is oily and unpleasant, it is known to be excellently nutritious and the blubber can be rendered down into a useful oil.

Carruthers harvested a large volume of native flora, which he hopes will prove efficacious in preventing further instances of scurvy. We tarried on the shore for another hour or two, for the days are growing long. Returned to the ship by midnight, well prepared to sail hard again tomorrow.

* * * * *

Surgeon's Log
28 July 1851

To land today in search of *Saxifraga punctata*, marsh fleabane (*Senecio congestus*), and coltsfoot (*Petasites frigiqys*). I confess absolute ignorance as to what such plants might look like, having only read about them in scientific papers, but Hall is, as always, more than happy to inform me of the depth of my witlessness and to redress it. He made several sketches for me, that I might be able to identify them, and went so far as to accompany me on the day's expedition, pointing out samples for my edification. Taylor informs me that that these plants can be made into a form of "sauerkraut" mixed with blubber; and that this concoction keeps Esquimeaux and white men alike quite free of the symptoms of scurvy. If I can convince the men to consume such a vile admixture, I shall conduct a small study. I certainly intend to take some myself.

* * * * *

Naturalist's Log
28 July 1851

The need for more extensive hunting works to my advantage, for it is doubtful we would have halted in our rapid progress westward for any other reason. As it is, I was able to spend a day ashore in a most interesting landscape. It was our first real expedition in many months; a vast relief to be off the ship in pleasant surroundings, and to be collecting new samples for analysis once more.

We made land on the northeast shore of Baring Island. The land was of bituminous slate. Further inland, dense columns of smoke issued from miniature volcanic mounds; not from any well-defined crater, but from their top, into which a pole could be thrust, as if into a cavity – so little adherent were its particles. Large masses of lime and sulphur, variously combined with other elements of the soil, including alum and silenito, could then be dug out.

The ground appeared as if in a state of fermentation, from the light, spongy nature of the soil, and so hot that we could not stand on it many minutes. These mounds formed quite a little amphitheatre, inclining from the sea at an angle of 45°, and elevated in height from 10 to 30 feet. There were several small rills of running water, elevated in temperature, in various states of combination with the substances mentioned. The general appearance conveyed to my mind an idea of similar chemical agency having previously existed on the bed of the ocean, prior to which, the sedimentary deposit from the super-incumbent water may have filled up the interstices of the cones, so as to impart that line of evenness and uniformity it now presents.

A little further along the shore, the seawater itself was steaming, the phenomenon I had observed inland having the effect of heating the sea in localized areas to temperatures varying between 143° in the most active areas and 104° towards the edges. The temperature of the unaffected seawater remains just slightly above freezing. I spent several hours taking samples and measurements that will, with careful analysis, enable me to fully document the phenomenon.

When I looked up from my work, the sun had dipped to the horizon and painted the sky in the oranges, pinks, and blues of the strange midnight twilight of the Arctic summer. Captain Maxwell was sitting on the beach watching me; I had no idea how long he had been there. He had brought me supper, for the men had lit a huge fire at our landing point and roasted several of the freshly snared hares. We ate together in silence, looking out over the strange landscape: rock and steam, ice and grass and crescent moon.

I have a new hypothesis, and that is that a sort of metamorphosis occurs in humans, as well as some animals. It happens to us invisibly, and often without volition, but it is inexorable when the necessary requirements for change are met. Those conditions, though, are different for each species, and for each individual man. My conditions are – I believe my conditions have been met.

* * * * *

Captain's Log
28 July 1851

A most satisfying expedition. The hunting party had excellent success, as did Carruthers and Hall in their various pursuits. When all the work of the day was finished, I permitted the men to remain ashore for several more hours, and when darkness fell they built up a large fire with driftwood scavenged from the beach and roasted several hares and two ptarmigan upon a carefully rigged spit, upon which they fell with good cheer and vigour.

I took one of the hares and walked half a mile up the beach to find Hall, who was still engrossed in his scientific activities. To my astonishment, the man had discovered a natural hot spring, and was crouched in the water, his clothing sopping wet, collecting samples. He becomes so absorbed in his work that he forgets all else, and then his face –

I made him come up to the beach and take a meal with me, for I knew for a fact that the man had eaten nothing all day. We passed a pleasant while together, but suddenly I became aware that he was shivering violently. The temperature is moderate now, and quite comfortable, but he remains grievously susceptible to cold after his ordeal on the ice. The breeze coming off the sea and his wet clothing had chilled him terribly.

The spectre of his discomfort made me decisive, even bold, for I cannot, with equanimity, see him suffer. I stood and began to pull off my clothing, setting it on the beach beside him.

"David?" he asked uncertainly, through chattering teeth.

"Come," I replied. "It is senseless to suffer when there is a remedy so near at hand. As for myself, I have not had a warm bath in well over a year."

And here I turned and strode into the water, quite naked. I should have called the rest of the party to join us, but ah! I felt so strange: both unlike myself, and more myself than I have ever been. I shrugged off Captain Maxwell for a time, and all of that man's cares. When the water reached nearly my waist, I dropped to sit. I was up to my neck in blissful heat, and I could not help but groan aloud at the profound comfort of it.

When I turned again to the shore, Embleton was standing, his body silhouetted against the muted colours of the summer night sky. Piece by piece, he pulled off his clothing and followed me into the water. I closed my eyes and heard him splash nearer. I resolved to be true.

He sat beside me, silently. I felt the moment his shivering finally subsided and his body relaxed into the warmth. His breathing was uneven. He slipped down further into the water, steam rising around him, until only his head was above the surface, reddish ringlets spread out on the surface of the water around him, alabaster skin rippling in the small waves.

"There were times during the winter when I thought I should never be warm again," I said.

He nodded. In the distance, a pair of ravens called to each other. "And yet, here we are," he replied. His voice was strangely hoarse.

"Here we are."

"I did not expect –" He paused, and turned to face me. We were very close. "Never in my life did I expect this."

I did not ask his meaning. "No more did I," I said, and then he reached for me, and caught my hand between his own, and brought it to his chest, over his heart, and I could feel it thrumming in the water.

"I am glad of it, though," he murmured, "whatever befalls us."

"Whatever befalls us," I agreed.

It was quite some time later when I came ashore, washed clean and glowing warm. I pulled on my clothes and jogged up the beach to call the rest of the shore party to come and bathe before our return to the ship. Embleton would not come out at all until the very last possible moment. Unexpectedly, he is a sensualist; he luxuriated in the warm water for as long as he could, staying well clear of the crew's delighted horseplay.

Whatever befalls us, there are moments of joy. We must seize them.

* * * * *

Surgeon's Log
29 July 1851

It is with a heavy heart that I make my first casualty report. We returned to the ship at approximately midnight to find that second mate Stephen Court had lapsed into a tubercular coma from which he did not awaken. I am inclined to doubt my decision to leave him under another's watch and go to shore, but then, there is nothing anyone could have done to prevent this outcome. Court took his last, painful breath at 08:18 this morning. I did not conduct an autopsy, as his cause of death was clear. Captain Maxwell ordered the body sewn up in canvas and placed in the dead room below deck; our first use of that terrible chamber. Court will be buried will all due honour when next we make land.

We are all solemn with this, our first loss.

✲ ✲ ✲ ✲ ✲

Death Notice
Gentleman's Magazine
August 1851

Mr. Michael Crawley, a frequent and most colourful contributor to the correspondence page of this periodical, entered into rest on 28 June, at home in London. His end was sudden after a lingering illness. Mr. Crawley was a well-respected man of business, and was predeceased by his wife in 1831. The funeral service was held at St. Aidan's; remains interred at Highgate. May God have especial pity on his daughter Hannah, and enable her to bear this sudden sorrow with Christian fortitude.

✲ ✲ ✲ ✲ ✲

Ship's Log
2 August 1851

This morning, the wind and water enabled us to fully traverse Prince of Wales Strait and put Baring Island firmly at our backs. We hug close to the shore of the coast, which is now Esquimeaux territory, unexplored by civilized man – or preceded only by Caulderson's expedition. Driftwood having been observed strewn in abundance along the beach, a boat was sent with Sugden (our carpenter) to procure some of it, and soon returned heavily laden; several pieces of which had such a fresh appearance that Mr. Sugden supposed it must have been felled recently. The view from the mast-head revealed to us the ice still unbroken far to the north. We were enveloped in a dense fog for the greater part of the day.

✲ ✲ ✲ ✲ ✲

Ship's Log
6 August 1851

Progress is slower than our passage through Parry Sound, but continues steadily along the coast. Our lookout in the masthead combs the shore for signs of Caulderson's expedition, but thus far fruitlessly.

At times, loose pieces of crumbling pack ice – sometimes as high as our quarter-boats – still undergoing the process of thaw, float down around us. Being generally loose, we pass harmlessly through it all. The ominous sounds of conflict forcibly remind us of last winter's adventures; but how changed is the sound, now comparatively subdued and soft, when contrasted with the hard, loud, grinding noises that heralded the onset of winter.

✲ ✲ ✲ ✲ ✲

Captain's Log
7 August 1851

Unless he has made the passage, he must be here. He must be close. And we must find him soon, or resign ourselves to another winter on the ice – and this more terrible than the last. I do not wish to lose more men on this mission, but we are all resolved to see it through. Even Hall, who previously had no interest in Caulderson or his crew, and who now has even less reason to wish for Caulderson's safe recovery, works tirelessly to aid the search, pouring over charts and expedition histories to ensure his predicted location is accurate. My feelings are – too vast to speak.

✲ ✲ ✲ ✲ ✲

Ship's Log
12 August 1851

The watch in the masthead has sighted a cairn ashore, just slightly west of where Sir Francis Hall and E. Hall each laid their mark upon the charts. There is a little bay, and the mouth of a wide river disappearing south into Esquimeaux lands. To the north remains a sea of ice that seems to never melt. We have but a narrow channel of open water between the two: can this be the route of the Passage? The fog has come up now, and we cannot risk sending the jolly to be lost in it. Tomorrow we shall see what the cairn has to tell us.

⁂ ⁂ ⁂ ⁂ ⁂

Naturalist's Log
13 August 1851

Up at 04:00 to row the jolly boat to shore along with a party of a dozen men. I confess, privately, to several unmeritorious sentiments, not least satisfaction in this confirmation of my deduction of Caulderson's chosen route. Satisfaction, but also some trepidation: it seems I have come to care about our collective mission slightly more than I intended or expected (which is to say, at all). In our short journey to shore, I espied several things that gave me pause; I held my tongue, however, as I had no wish to alarm the captain before it was absolutely necessary. On the shore, butted up against the scrubby brush, were bits of wood and detritus that looked, to me, not natural in shape or origin.

The general aspect everywhere in this region presents the same character of Arctic starkness, but here it is more generally bold and lofty in its outline, and the land more elevated. There is an estuary in the little bay, and then hills rising up on either side of the river, so lofty in some places as to be nearly vertical, rising to a height from 200 to 300 feet. The eastern slopes have their escarpment formed of a hard frozen snow, contrasting forcibly with the denuded wild appearance presented by those with a western front. Evidently, prevailing winds are from the east.

The soil is composed of a scoriaceous admixture with large stones and boulders plentifully strewn over its surface; the latter has a uniform covering of granite, quartz, clay-slate, and other pebbles, with a few scanty tufts of hardy grasses and other Arctic plants interspersed throughout. In the little valleys running perpendicular to the shore, nature appears to be more lavish of her gifts. Favoured by the shelter afforded by the neighbouring hills, and by the melting of the summer's snow, I collected samples of numerous plants and small flowering shrubs that I have not seen described in the literature of the region. It is most thrilling.

I am sorry – to my own surprise, I am very sincerely sorry – for the contents of our other discovery.

* * * * *

Ship's Log
13 August 1851

Ashore early with a party of a dozen men. In the clear morning air, we found the cairn easily, and it was the work of an hour to dig out the message. The instant it was placed in my hands, I could perceive that some terrible decline had taken place in the interval between this and the leaving of the previous messages, for this was not a neatly-written letter with careful records appended. This was little more than a sheaf of scattered papers, torn and ragged and rolled together in a bit of shirt cotton. Message as appended here.

* * * * *

Record deposited by Captain William Caulderson
Formerly, HMS Vanguard
15 July 1850
Camp Vanguard: 135.7°W; 70.1°N

[First fragment, seemingly torn from a larger book]

shore this morning, one of the seamen informed me that strangers were seen from the observatory. I proceeded accordingly in the direction pointed out, and soon saw four Esquimeaux near a small iceberg, not far from the land, and about a mile from the ship. They retreated behind it as soon as they perceived me; but as I approached the whole party came suddenly out of their shelter, forming a body of ten in front and three deep. I hailed them, and was answered by a general shout of the same kind. The rest of my party now coming up, we

[several lines obscured by water damage]

frozen in quite irreversibly

[several lines obscured by water damage]

this, they threw their knives and spears in the air in every direction, returning the shout and extending their arms to show that they also were without weapons. But as they did not quit their places, we advanced, and embraced in succession all those in the front line, stroking down their dress also, and receiving from them in return this established ceremony of friendship. This seemed to produce great

[Second fragment:]

all carried spears with shafts formed of small pieces of wood or bone joined expertly together. Having no foresight of these visitors we had of course no presents at hand for them, and we therefore sent a man back to the ship for 31 pieces of iron hoop, that there might be a gift for each individual. But in the meantime they consented to accompany us on board.

A lively trade has now begun. The savages come daily with food – more than enough to sustain us, although we have not found ways to prepare the seal and walrus meat palatably. We pay for this sustenance in metal, knives, needles, and barrel hoops. If we can find ways to preserve the meat in quantity, we shall be adequately provisioned for the next leg of the journey northwest, if ever the damnable ice will thaw.

[Third fragment:]

demonstrate how a gun could hit hard at close range. When they saw the rock shatter, the Esquimeaux ran away. We anticipate no more trouble of the sort wi

[Fourth fragment:]

Captain's Log
7 February 1849

In the past month, the Esquimeaux have brought us for barter: two white bears, a dozen foxes, and fifty seals. We have come to a perfect understanding respecting the price of each article, and hope that the constant pilfering is at an end.

I was at first astonished to see so many young wives and mothers amongst the traders, and in such fine appearance and expression; many with large, dark, sparkling eyes, beautiful pearl-like teeth, most luxuriant raven-black hair, small and delicately-formed hands and feet. These women are radiant with smiles of cheerful good-humour, and excite the interest of some of the men.

There is danger in this, as we are now on more intimate terms; and they invited us up to the encampment; but our interpreter did not consider it prudent, from what he judged of their character, to accept the invitation. We therefore stay with the ship, approached constantly by all the men, women and children – a wild and picturesque party. Each of us appears to have a group of followers; the women laying hold of our arms, and attempting to walk with us – a degree of familiarity it is not safe to allow with a people generally treacherous and deceitful. While thus walking, some of our people had their pockets picked, the thief taking advantage of their arms being held by the women.

[Fifth fragment:]

Ship's Log
29 July 1850

Still not the remotest sign of thaw and we remain held tight by the ice. Even the old ice master has not seen a year like this. Dropped to half rations. Morale low; several men very ill with tubercular coughs and scorbutic haemorrhage. The sick list

[Sixth fragment:]

orning, Mr. Mackenzie discovered that his whale-bone ship's knife had been stolen, and recovered it in the Esquimeaux camp beside the ship. By way of punishment, the offender was consigned to solitary confinement for some hours in the ship's coal-hole. As, however, the Esquimeaux only laughed at this as a very good joke, I determined to treat the entire company as seamen under my command, and administered naval discipline: the delinquent was put down into the store-room and closely confined for several hours; when having collected several of the natives on board, I ordered him to be stripped in their presence and to receive a dozen lashes on the back with a cat-o-nine-tails. He was then confined again for a night before we released him. Perhaps this will have the desired effect, and the Esquimeaux can be pacified with discipline where trade and friendship have failed to have a civilizing influen

[Seventh fragment:]

whether to press forward or to double back and retrieve the cached foods we deposited early in our voyage. Yesterday a hunting party went out and an affray ensued, in which three of the natives lost their lives. The men, it appeared, having surrounded a small lake to secure some wild fowl, were surprised by a party of Esquimeaux, and at once retreated. The natives in following them fired a few arrows, upon which the men turned, and discharging their guns, killed three of the party, and might possibly have wounded others. The natives, thoroughly dismayed at seeing their countrymen fall around them, fled in the greatest disorder; and the men, equally alarmed, betook themselves to flight also. Our trade and good relations are unlikely to

[Eighth fragment, badly crumpled and water damaged:]

the ice was slowly crushing it, the men all worked for their lives in getting out provisions; but, before they could save much, the ice turned the vessel down on its side, snapping the masts and breaking a hole in her bottom so overwhelming that she sank at once, before I could even give the order to abandon ship. Several men at work could not get out in time, and were carried down with her and drowned. Two more froze to death in the aftermath. Many more are likely now to die of starvation, for we had not had time to get provisions out of her.

This is surely the worst moment in my

[Final fragment:]

wooden shelter here, to pass a fourth winter. Then march south with the river, and hope to encounter Indian encampments to lead us to a northern trading post.

[Writing on paper wrapper:]

If this record is found, be it noted here that it is my belief that the Northwest Passage will be discovered by following the stretch of open water west between the continental shore and the impenetrable ice pack to the north. It will be for those who follow us to confirm our suspicion and complete our mission of discovery, which we have only partly fulfilled. We will follow the river south as long as we can walk: myself, Mackenzie, Davidson, Blythe, Surbaugh, Jeffries, Clinker, Donnelly, Fitzgerald, Rogers, and young Charles. We are now the only survivors.

✲ ✲ ✲ ✲ ✲

Erktua, who was a witness, speaks of the qallunaat disaster at Tuktuujaqrtuuq

Ootook, a superior annatko, angered the qallunaat at Tuktuujaqrtuuq by taking a shovel to use at his own iglu. The qallunaat are vengeful. They caused him to be whipped with something that was made of ropes with knots in them. The Inuit who were forced to witness this wanted to help Ootook defend himself, but he told them, "Let the qallunaat try to kill me; they cannot, for I am an annatko." Then Ootook's hands were untied, after which the qallunaat tried to cut his hands and head with long knives. Every time a blow was struck, the extreme end of the blade came close to Ootook's throat; occasionally the blade came just above the crown of his head. But after all he was uninjured because he is very powerful. This is what we saw. Then they put him back in the dark hole. After Ootook had been one day and one night in the dark hole, he thought he would use his power to destroy the vessel by splitting it through the middle from stem to stern. So he commenced calling to his aid the Good Spirit, when a great crackling noise was made, now and then, under the ship, and at the end of the day of confinement, the qallunaat, fearing from such great and terrific noises that the ship would be destroyed, let Ootook go.

That night, the ice started to crack and break all around the qallunaat ship. They became excited, and prepared themselves to leave, but Ootook sat and laughed at them. While they were getting ready, even though the weather was so calm, pieces of wood started coming out from under the boat, floating up and mixing with the ice. Pamiuluq, the one with the bad tail, was chewing up the boat, taking those pieces of wood out from under the water and the ice. The qallunaat did not notice their ship was breaking apart. They were rushing, probably because they had not seen a thaw in so long. All of a sudden the ship completely broke apart. Steam and smoke came out of it. The weather was calm, so even though we were far away from it, we could see the smoke. Many of the qallunaat sank into the water with the ship and drowned, and the water under the ice was so cold that some of them died of it. A few made it to land, and there was much discussion amongst the Inuit about what we would do about that. In the end, we decided to leave them to themselves: not help them, and not kill them. We will see what they can make of themselves, these mighty qallunaat.

⚬ ⚬ ⚬ ⚬ ⚬

Captain's Log
13 August 1851

It is terrible to read such deterioration, and worse still to imagine such events. I feel I have been numb since the discovery of the cairn, as if touched by bitter cold. Can – can he yet live? Would something deep within me not know, if he were dead?

Hall says that we should take hope from this: we are close. Whatever has happened, we are close to the end, now. His hand on my wrist is the only bit of warmth remaining, and how I cling to it.

⚬ ⚬ ⚬ ⚬ ⚬

Personal Diary
Hannah Crawley
14 August 1851

I am ruined. He has left me nothing but creditors. Every post brings more. I thought I would be free, but I am exactly as free as a caged bird, slamming itself again and again into the wire mesh of its cage. I cannot think –

I am ruined. Lew is gone, dead or gone – it matters little which. I have been a very great fool, I see that now – and Father is gone, and I am ruined. What am I to do?

⁂ ⁂ ⁂ ⁂ ⁂

Ship's Log
15 August 1851

Stephen Court was today interred on a rising ground a few hundred yards from the sea to the southwest of the ship. Mr. Wynniatt gave a reading and the crew sang a hymn. I performed my office, reciting words too familiar to sailors: "We therefore commit his body to the earth, to be turned into corruption, looking for the resurrection of the body and the life of the world to come, through our Lord Jesus Christ; who at His coming shall change our vile body, that it may be like His glorious body, according to the mighty working whereby He is able to subdue all things unto Himself." May I never be required to say these words again; they are terrible for a captain to speak. And then I must reflect upon how often Captain Caulderson must have recited the same words, and I sorrow for him, and with him. A handsome tomb of stone and mortar was built over the spot, having at one end a stone let in, with the usual information engraved on it. The sides were plastered with a kind of viscous clay found in one of the ponds – Hall would know the exact type. The top covered with tufts of the purple saxifrage.

In the midst of life we are in death.

Chapter Seven: August – October 1851

Ship's Log
16 August 1851

Planning underway for an overland rescue mission following Caulderson and his ten remaining crewmen south along the path of the great river. We shall resume our search for the Passage only after Caulderson is located; a man's life must surely take precedence over any other mission. Mr. Taylor departed this morning with an advance scouting party (Sainsbury and Wilcox). They will march hard for five days up the river, making all possible haste. We anticipate their progress at 30 miles per day (surely much more than the sick and starving *Vanguard* survivors would be able to make). At the end of their fifth day (at 150 miles south from the coast), they will deposit a secure cache of supplies (rations to last four men ten days, blankets, slops, and ammunition), and then return to the ship, halting only to hunt when they can. Upon their return, Taylor will assume command.

Meanwhile, I am preparing a four-man rescue party, to be led by myself. Our packs will contain pemmican and hardtack enough for a month, which we will supplement with hunting as we can. Ammunition, warm and waterproof clothing, and canvas tents (one large, and one small spare) we will also carry. We depart early tomorrow. The party will consist of myself, Henry Sugden, Peter Thompson, and Embleton Hall. The former two are selected for their physical strength and endurance: we do not know in what physical condition we may find our quarry, and if it becomes necessary to haul injured men, Sugden and Thompson can haul more than any other man aboard. Naturalist Hall's knowledge of the environs and his keen eye are invaluable tracking tools; he is also eager to see the interior of the continent.

⁂ ⁂ ⁂ ⁂ ⁂

Captain's Log
16 August 1851

The plan, I believe, is sound. If the *Vanguard* survivors were unable to procure supplies and ammunition from their sinking ship, they cannot have got far. They cannot be hunting much, and may not even have adequate tents for shelter. Unless they have made peace with the savage tribe of which Caulderson wrote, they must be close to starving. Soon they will be freezing. Every day, now – every hour – could be the difference between life and death for them. But at least now there is something I can do.

⁂ ⁂ ⁂ ⁂ ⁂

Overland Expedition Log
Recorded by David Maxwell, Captain, Serapis
18 August 1851

Yesterday, the day of our departure from the *Serapis*, was mild, with the thermometer reaching as high as 59°, and very sunny. To make most haste, we dispensed with the usual overland sledge and carry only what we can fit in our packs. We have not had reason to regret this decision, although Hall is unsurprisingly voluble in bemoaning his lack of proper scientific apparatuses.

⁂ ⁂ ⁂ ⁂ ⁂

Dearest Lew,

I sat down to say a great deal – my heart was full – I did not know what to say first – and grief, and confusion, and (O my head) I cannot tell what – and though, and grief, and confusion, came crowding so thick upon me; one would be first; another would be first; all would be first; so I can write nothing at all. – Only that, whatever has happened to me, I cannot tell; my supposed advantages became a snare to me. *Pretty*? What is pretty? Clever? *Kind*? It is nothing but waiting and waiting and more waiting, and all the while – Yes, but I am; for I am still, and I ever will be,

Your true –

H

⁂ ⁂ ⁂ ⁂ ⁂

Innugati whispers the story of Sedna to her daughters
At Kangiqtugaapik when the sky was bright

Many people tell many stories, and all of them are true. There are many stories of Sedna. This one is true, too.

There were a few families living together near Qikiqtarjuaq. They moved with the seasons to hunt beluga whales on the coast and caribou and musk ox on the tundra. Then one day, one of the hunters was careless. He was mauled by a walrus and died, leaving his wife, Sedna, alone.

The woman was forced to depend upon charity. She became a burden of which the other families wished to rid themselves. So they put all her belongings into their umiak and one day when they were at sea they seized Sedna and cast her overboard. She struggled to regain the side of the boat and when she seized it they cut off her fingers.

Sedna, in her despair, screamed for vengeance as she sank under the waves. Her severed thumb became a walrus, her first finger a seal, and her middle finger a white bear.

And now, when the former two animals see a man they try to escape, lest they be served as the woman was. The white bear lives both on the land and on the sea, and when she perceives a man, rage fills her and she determines to kill the person, who she thinks destroyed the woman from whose fingers she sprang.

Sedna will always have her revenge.

* * * * *

Ship's Log
First Mate Lew Taylor writing
25 August 1851

Advance scouting mission came off passing well. Supplies for rescue party's return cached approximately 165 miles south off the coast on the great river. Party returned in good health, self included; we passed the Captain's party shortly after noon on 22 August. All making excellent progress. It is well we did not attempt to row the dinghy up the river, as some suggested, for the current is swift and there are many rocky rapids. Discovered the remains of an old Esquimeaux encampment about two days' journey south: two mounds of a circular form a few yards apart, and around each six heads of musk oxen were embedded in the soil. Nearby we found numerous bones of reindeer, foxes, and birds strewn about, much bleached from long exposure. We found no other signs of human habitation.

* * * * *

Surgeon's Log
27 August 1851

My previous harvest of antiscorbutics proving most efficacious, the healthy men are daily sent ashore to gather sorrel. I have ample evidence of the beneficial effects resulting from its use; as of this date I can clearly discern an improvement in the general appearance of the men, and the majority express themselves as feeling generally better than they had felt a month previous. The quantity obtained is such as to afford a small allowance to each man daily, after the wants of the sickest are supplied. Sorrel, when eaten alone, or with the addition of a little vinegar and mustard, forms a most agreeable and excellent salad, highly relished and eagerly sought for by all.

We are also able to procure ducks, geese, and occasionally even eggs, which the men are permitted to retain for mess in addition to regular rations, with the result being that most have regained the weight they lost during the winter and are recovering superbly.

I am pleased to report that the sick list (appended) is dwindling.

* * * * *

Overland Expedition Log
Resumed
28 August 1851

Our days begin to shape themselves into a recognizable routine. We wake at 05:30 to break our fast, fold up our tent, and are generally on the march by 06:00, taking luncheon (two squares of hardtack and whatever we manage to save from the previous night's dinner) at midday, stopping only to fill our flasks with water from the river. The way forward is not difficult, the riverbank being largely free of obstructions that would halt our progress. Vegetation here is mainly low shrubbery, and the walking is easy. We do not halt until 19:00 or 20:00, when Hall and I pitch the tent and build a fire, and Sugden and Thompson take rifles or a fishing line and attempt to find something with which to supplement our evening rations of hardtack and pemmican. Sometimes Hall discovers some edible berries or salad leaves, and these provide welcome variety. Our exertions during the day have us tumbling into our blankets immediately after our meal. The next day, we do the same again.

30 August 1851

There was a fog yesterday, with the thermometer falling, which somewhat impeded our march, but by the late afternoon it was sunny and fine. We are often able to reach our daily goal of 30 miles, by my estimation.

3 September 1851

A shower of rain fell steadily this day, soaking through our clothing and blankets. We are quite miserable, but as long as we keep on the move, we stay warm enough. We have seen no sign of the party we are pursuing – even Hall is perplexed. If they had been here, I feel certain Hall's powers of observation would discover evidence of that fact. Perhaps they branched off from the river path that we follow? And yet, why would they? For the river makes its way south, and allows for easy walking. Still, if their scurvy is advanced, as it must be after so many years, their minds may be compromised. It is a great worry.

5 September 1851

Yesterday ended in a clear northerly gale, so cold that the rain which had fallen during the day froze on the ground overnight. The highest degree of the thermometer being but 30°, and the lowest was 27°. With sheer ice now coating the ground, the chances of disastrous injury increase tenfold. Traversing such a landscape is almost insuperably difficult; and the whole progress that we could make in the morning was but four miles. Luckily, the sun emerged from the clouds around noon, and the ice soon melted, making travel again possible. If we meet with such conditions again, Hall suggests that we drive nails through the soles of our boots, although I fear the resultant damp would but add to our discomfort.

7 September 1851

This morning, we woke shivering and were obliged to dig the tent out of the snow before we could proceed. It had stormed during the night, and the temperature plunged to such a degree that sleet had turned to ice and snow, and we were too exhausted to notice. Our road was at first much encumbered with wreaths of snow from the gale, but by noon the weather had changed again, and the snow melted away in temperatures well above 40°, so that we were forced to remove our thick woolen outercoats and walk in our shirtsleeves. It was an excellent demonstration, and reminder, of the changeable nature of Arctic climes.

8 September 1851

We must decrease our consumption of the dwindling ship's rations; or stop them altogether if at all possible. We will not turn 'round again and head north to the ship until we have located our quarry. We shall halt earlier in the day and allow more time for hunting. Today Evans bagged a brace of hares, and we eat heartily for now.

10 September 1851

Hall has discovered a fire pit and campsite in a small natural hollow on the riverbank. He thinks it to be many months old, and to have been inhabited by five or ten men, European, but it is difficult to say with certainty. As it was near to our usual stopping time, we set up camp in the very spot.

⁂ ⁂ ⁂ ⁂ ⁂

Captain's Log
12 September 1851

As we walk, words come easier. One foot in front of the other, one word follows the next, and none to see my face as I speak it. I should perhaps not say that it is easier – but it is less difficult. This afternoon there came a time when Hank and Peter were up 50 yards ahead, and Embleton just behind me, bringing up the rear. We had been silent for some time. The monotony of the march can sometimes induce a contemplative state, and so it had worked on me. Without thinking – without planning it – I found myself opening my mouth and speaking to Embleton about Caulderson: about William and I, and how we were together. There is a – a cold, dead weight in feeling such things, and never being able to speak them. I *can* speak them, to Em. God! There is no police to arrest me, no court to try me; there is no naval authority here to hang me, for *I am* the authority. I shall never be freer, and perhaps never speak so freely. I told him about our first meeting, and about the strange sympathy that seemed to exist between us from the start. I – I told him our story, every bit of it.

He listened. He did not pull back in disgust, nor did he scoff or flush or rage. He was kind. He was so very kind.

And then, giddy with the relief of being *heard* – I kept on. I told him things I have not even told Addie about that terrible night in Guadeloupe when our ship took fire in the dead of night. I told him how, when I woke to find my cabin full of smoke, my first thought was of William. I told him how I ran to his cabin, how I found him ablaze and screaming. How the flesh hung off his face. How I see it now, in my dreams. How I grabbed him and smothered the flames, dragging him out even as he ordered me to leave him, to go back for Cookie and Fred – and Christ! – little Paulie on the orlop deck! How his orders turned to pleas, and how he *begged* me to see to his men and leave him. How I would not – would *not* until he was on the dock, safe, far away from the flaming ship. And how by then, it was too late for the rest.

And then – the recriminations. The things he said to me in his grief, and in his shame and sorrow and pain. "This is God's punishment, visited upon us," he said. "You should have let me die." "We should both be dead, if there were any justice in the world." And worst of all, the words I hear in my dreams: "You let them die, against my orders. You are a murderer, David."

I think I feared that, hearing all, Embleton too would think me a murderer. I shuddered with that fear, and that shame, and he was silent.

One foot in front of the other.

I could not see his face.

Suddenly, hands grabbed at my shoulders and spun me around; Hall stepped close and lobbed a series of strange questions at me, almost too rapidly to take in.

"From what type of wood was the ship built? How old was it? Had it ever been dry-docked? What was the precise distance between cabins? How many paces? How were the decks partitioned? How long did it take to sink? How did the other men escape? Why did Cookie and Chester not hear the alarm? Why was the boy in the orlop? What size were the bulkheads? Oho! Of what were they composed? Were your stores full, or depleted? Were the bedclothes of cotton? Linen? Wool? With what fabric was your clothing was made?" It went on and on, and I stammered out answers as best I could.

He was silent then for several minutes, and we resumed our pace, which had fallen off during our conversation. Our companions were almost out of sight ahead of us.

I glanced at him then. His lips were moving and he was muttering calculations to himself as he often does when he's thinking hard.

Suddenly, he stopped dead in his tracks. "It would have happened anyway, David. They would have died either way – and had you gone back for them, you would have died with them, and Caulderson too."

"How – how can you know that?" I asked. Was this some poor attempt at comfort, this condescension? A wave of nameless emotion washed over me.

All at once, I was burning with rage. I grabbed onto his coat and shook him, hard. "*How can you know?*"

He rolled his eyes and had the temerity to look offended by my skepticism. "I calculated from the natural facts, David. My opinion is scientifically sound, I assure you."

I looked at him in astonishment for a full minute. And then I was laughing – laughing and crying and embracing him, all at once.

I could not speak coherently, and he looked rather taken aback at my response. Suddenly, he threw back his head and laughed, as well. Why, I do not know – nor, I suspect, does he. But I know that it was healing to laugh so, with him.

Can he – truly – be correct? God knows, I've never had cause to doubt his scientific acumen. I will think long and hard upon his words.

* * * * *

Overland Expedition Log
Resumed
17 September 1851

We are one month into our overland expedition, and must soon decide whether to return to the ship or risk being caught in the grip of an Arctic winter without the protections the ship affords. It is unlikely in the extreme that we could survive a full season of such exposure. The same, however, might be said of Caulderson and his men, who have already survived a winter since the *Vanguard* went down.

23 September 1851

The thermometer at night is about the freezing point. For the last two days we have made very slow progress; being compelled by the irregularities of the riverbank to perform circuits and navigate around obstacles, including some rocky and impassible cliffs. In 11 hours today, we traversed perhaps as few as 10 miles. The river's path grows ever more treacherous.

27 September 1851

Progress continues slow. In our march today, we passed many small bays and points of land, and saw the blue mountains to the westward, perhaps five or six miles distant. Game remains plentiful, and we have been able to forgo ship's rations for over a week.

⚬ ⚬ ⚬ ⚬ ⚬

Naturalist's Log
27 September 1851

It was too tempting an opportunity to pass up. When the other three were safely snoring in their blankets, I exited the tent (for I had contrived to position myself nearest the entrance) and pulled on my slops. I require less sleep than other men, and I did not wish to trouble them, for they would be worried about my becoming lost – but it is a clear night, with moon and stars and bright aurora. I could not possibly lose my way. And the mountains are so close! I could not pass over the opportunity to observe them; to my knowledge, this part of the world has never been surveyed, and I shall chart as much of it as I can.

I followed the river upstream for a little more than an hour, and there I discovered a small tributary branching off to the southeast.

It struck me then quite forcibly that – idiotic though he has certainly been about a certain David Maxwell, the kindest, best, and bravest man to ever walk the earth – William Caulderson is a man highly knowledgeable in naval history. Such a man would not undertake an expedition to the Arctic without reading all previous expedition logs. Would he not see this little tributary as a potential route southeast to the ironically-named Camp Victory, where Captain Montgomery Smith had cached supplies during his fateful expedition of 1834? Would he not take the gamble that a mere 100 miles of riverbed trekking to the southeast would bring him and his men to a store of food and supplies that could mean the difference between life and death to them?

I am willing to bet that he would take that gamble – but I shall present the idea to Captain Maxwell in the morning, and we shall see what he makes of it.

I took the usual measurements and observations, and ascertained the general figure and extent of the tributary, scouting up as far as I thought prudent. It is evidently a shallow piece of water. I then returned to camp for a few hours of sleep.

✲ ✲ ✲ ✲ ✲

Overland Expedition Log
Resumed
28 September 1851

Based upon new information provided by naturalist Hall (who has apparently taken it upon himself to act as party scout), we today turned off from the main river and headed southeast along a small tributary, believing the Caulderson group may be making for a cache of food and provisions left by the Smith expedition of 1834. It is a sound theory, for Caulderson has a comprehensive knowledge of the naval history of the Arctic, and surely has a mental map of every cache known to exist within 1000 miles.

Before turning from our intended path, I ordered a large cairn of rocks piled up, and deposited a message with details as to our new route. If we should be lost, Taylor will at least find us easy to track.

Thus buoyed up with new hope, we marched hard for four or five hours in a southeasterly direction. The path grew rocky and difficult as we entered the foothills of the mountains we had observed yesterday.

At approximately 13:45, Sugden – who was then acting as point-man and marching almost a half mile ahead of the rest of us – whooped an alert. We rushed forward to meet him, our hearts in our throats, to find him standing beside a tumbled-down cairn built in the European style. Wordlessly, he pointed at a small piece of wood that had been fashioned into the shape of a cross. A Christian grave, then, but a nameless one. We removed our hats.

After a few moments of respectful silence, I ordered a sweep of the area. Perhaps there would be other indications of the survivors – perhaps even a message deposited somewhere close by. I sent Hall upriver, while Sugden, Thompson, and I fanned out from the bank. We were to walk one hour, and then turn back to our meeting place. As it turns out, though, it was less than 10 minutes later that Thompson's strong halloo called us all back.

We found him standing speechless in the middle of a silent, shabby habitation – it could hardly be called a camp. There was a single, ragged tent – naval issue – standing on the top of some rising ground. The tent itself was large and made with a ridge pole resting on a perpendicular pole at the other end – small ropes extended from top tent at each end to the ground where the rope ends were fast to sticks that had been driven into the ground. There was a fire pit with an abandoned kettle a few yards from the tent, and some small detritus still scattered about. No one answered our calls. Sugden poked his head into the tent, and came reeling back looking stricken. Thompson absently poked at something with his booted foot, and jumped back in alarm when Hall bent to pick it up, for it was a human skull.

What we discovered today was horror: the bodies of the dead, and no living men. Some of the bodies lay in the tent, others were scattered about in different directions. This was bad enough – but there was worse to come. For from the mutilated state of many of the bodies, and the contents of the kettle, it is evident that our wretched countrymen had been driven to the last dread alternative as a means of sustaining life.

In the tent we found blankets, bedding, and several skeleton bones – bones with no flesh, nothing except sinews attached to them. One body lay on the floor, looking flayed, and preserved horribly by the cold. A final man lay on the ground on his back. He must have been the last to die, for his body alone is unmarked. I do not recognize his features; he is, at least, not Caulderson.

We retreated back to the stone cairn after making a careful search for any survivors – of which there is no indication. None of us wished to stay in that terrible place any longer than necessary. We must sleep; none of us wants a meal now. We will sleep, and hope for an absence of dreams, and when we wake we shall attempt to understand this chaos. I will have Hall conduct a detailed examination, first, for we must learn all we can about the circumstances leading up to this tragedy, and if any man can endure such a task, it surely is he. While he does his work, the rest of us shall perform our final solemn mission task, and begin to dig some graves.

✲ ✲ ✲ ✲ ✲

The annatko tells what happened to Aklaq at the qallunaat death camp near Kittigazuit

Aklaq and her son went to the tent and among the frozen mass of human bones and bodies that were lying around it she saw one qallunaat body that had a bright white chain around the neck. She knew at once that it was made of precious metal, for some of the other Inuit had come into possession of similar qallunaat treasures by way of trade or discovery. The body of this man was lying on one side, and was imbedded in solid ice from head to feet. The way the chain was about the neck and running down one side of the body indicated that there was more beneath it; and therefore, to remove it, she found a difficult and disagreeable task before her. Neither she nor her son had any tools with them; therefore, while the son was seeking around, she procured a heavy sharp stone, and with this chipped away the ice from all round the body until it was released.

Aklaq could never forget the dreadful, fearful feeling she had all the time while engaged doing this; for, besides the tent being filled with frozen corpses – some entire and some mutilated with flesh cut off with knives and hatchets – this man who had the metal she sought seemed to her to have been the last that died, and his face was just as though he were only asleep. All the while she was at work breaking the ice near the head, especially the ice about the face, she felt great horror, and for this reason had to stop several times. She was very careful not to touch any part of the body while pounding with the sharp stone, and thus risk angering the spirit Atshen who lived in this place now, possessing men with his evil and compelling them to consume their brothers. At last, after having pounded away the ice from around and under the body, her son helped her to lift it out of its icy bed, and finally remove the chain from the frozen garments in which the body was completely dressed.

* * * * *

Naturalist's Log
29 September 1851

There are significant difficulties inherent in performing any scientific analysis of this tableau, although I am attempting to be as accurate as possible: there is the evidence of the actions of men who died here, and this is overlaid with evidence of extensive animal activity, of climactic variability, of the passage of time, and then of other human intervention, for I believe at least one Esquimeau has been here since the men all died.

I am recording all evidence in detailed field notes (appended). There is a strange and keen satisfaction in reading the stories told by the bones.

We discovered one body in the cairn about 50 yards outside the camp – probably the first of the survivors to die. This evidence of Christian burial indicates that the site was occupied for a prolonged period. In the beginning, the situation may not have been so desperate, but it grew worse with time, as the men sickened and starved. This much is clear to me: the men who died inside the tent were the perpetrators of cannibalism. Although many of the remains in the tent were mutilated, that damage was mostly done post-mortem by foxes or wolves. The sawed and cracked bones found in the kettle were from other bodies, which were discarded outside the tent. As would be expected, the macabre work of dismemberment was done outside. There is a large stump that has been used as a sort of butcher block.

One other thing is clear, and it is vital. *There are not enough bodies to account for all the* Vanguard *survivors.* There is the intact, frozen body in the tent, and also there the flayed body. The grave under the cairn contains one body, three skulls were discovered strewn about in the ice and snow outside the tent, and two others – in the kettle. That is eight men accounted for, and we track 11.

It is a vast relief to me that I have some good news to share with David. He is almost catatonic with the horror of it, moving like an automaton. Perhaps this will shake him into action, which is where he thrives. I shall strive to help him focus his energies on what must now be done, and take upon myself the task of cataloging the terrible events of the past.

✻ ✻ ✻ ✻ ✻

The annatko continues, after telling Aklaq's story:

We watched these bad qallunaat for many days. Erktua, who watched the qallunaat's umiak sink beneath the sea at Tuktuujaqrtuuq, said they were harmless now, that they would die soon, but I do not think that they are ever harmless, and I followed them. I tracked them and looked in on them as they made their slow, slow trek to the south. Aklaq and her son came with me sometimes, and sometimes I went alone, or they did. I wanted to make sure they were truly harmless, or I would kill them myself.

Even before they made their death camp, some of them already seemed ill. They were very thin, and their mouths were hard and black. They had no fur clothing on, and no snow goggles. Sometimes Aklaq's son would feel pity, watching them, and would try to help, but they refused. They would grab at him and burst out screaming in words we could not understand. So we left them to themselves, and only watched them.

After a while, their movements became very slow. They stopped for some days and made their camp. Three of them brought wood and meat to the camp while the others stayed inside. One man died, and they buried him there, under the earth, right outside camp, his head pointing east. They did not even perform naasiivik, and that is when their camp became a death camp.

After that, the three strongest men departed, moving south along the river. We decided to let them go. They were dying. They were all dying.

* * * * *

Captain's Log
30 September 1851

I must make plans. Hall asks for instructions. I must master myself. I should have considered this eventuality, but – *Caulderson*? He, so good and honorable? He who strives always to be better? I cannot think of this horror and that man as anything but diametrically opposed. The man I know cannot have countenanced this.

My mind is – it is in disarray, and will not obey my wishes. It will only tell me terrible stories about what has happened here, dark imaginings that leave me retching and shaking in the snow.

Some of the larger thigh bones have been cracked, to get at the marrow. Some of the skulls have holes punched in them – with an ice chisel, Embleton thinks – to get at

I cannot –

Did he…? I cannot believe it of him, but then again – *wouldn't I*?

We pitch our tent 200 yards upriver. I will not spend a night in this place of the dead.

* * * * *

Ship's Log
Taylor writing
30 September 1851

The ice master has kept a careful eye to the sea, but our channel thus far remains open, despite occasional formations of young ice and even pancake ice. We send scouts south along the river every day with instructions to fire off shots at regular intervals, but no sign of the rescue party's return yet appears. I find it prudent to prepare for another winter here on the ice. This little bay provides more protection from the elements than did our last wintering location, and game is more plentiful.

Every able man is now engaged in hunting and fishing, and every sick man has a hand in butchering or salting the meat. We must increase our stores substantially. I wish to have nothing but positive reports for Captain Maxwell upon his return.

* * * * *

Ship's Log
Taylor writing
1 October 1851

At 02:00 this morning, and with shocking force, the ice was upon us. Warde on watch in the crow's nest failed to call a warning before a large berg knocked us violently from the north. All rushing on deck, we saw that in order to prevent the ship from being driven onshore, we had to maintain our connexion with the berg; this was strengthened by many halsers and a stream chain, two of which were passed round it and secured. In this state we were still borne onward, about 80 yards from the shore, the ship sustaining heavy pressure particularly at stern and rudder – the latter was seriously damaged. Numerous large masses were sunk beneath the ship in the frightful melee in which we were engaged, when about 04:45 it temporarily subsided. She then lay perfectly cradled in the ice, huge masses of it having been forced under her keel, which raised her three feet at the bow, and upwards of five feet at the stern. Masses of flinty hardness still pressing heavily on the port side, banked us up between them and the berg, which threw the ship over several degrees; and thus in utter helplessness we awaited the next movement.

In the meantime, the state of the rudder demanded our attention – it was already damaged, and its safety still further jeopardized by the heavy blocks of ice that surrounded it. To unship it was then our object, but the ice completely blocked it up and this became extremely difficult. Some of the ice was removed by pickaxe and ice chisels, but it was ultimately found necessary to have recourse to gunpowder for clearing away the remainder.

We were loath to attempt such a dangerous maneuver without our blasting expert Hall, but Clem Basting has been his reluctant protégé in much of the ice work, and supervised the blast most satisfactorily. After some hours work, we succeeded in extricating the rudder; this ponderous, unwieldy implement was placed on the deck, and the carpenter commenced the necessary repairs.

I shall never forget the sensation I experienced during the short period of this terrible conflict. Every timber in the ship groaned in the most direful and ominous language of complaint, the masts shook, and as I stood on the quarter-deck, the planks beneath my feet vibrated. And I – I responsible.

The ship has been carried from 10 fathoms water into three-and-a-half; but is nowhere in contact with the shore, as she is now perfectly cradled in the ice. In this state we remain. I've ordered all hands to keep knapsacks in readiness for any sudden emergency. The remainder of the day, one of anxiety and watching, closed in cold, wild, cheerless, and squally.

It is now clear that the season for navigating the ice-bound sea has drawn to a close. The first operation of a ship going into winter quarters has therefore now commenced, under my orders, with the making of the fire-hole. In doing so we penetrated four-and-a-half feet of closely-packed ice before reaching the water – the depth of the cradle in which the ship now lies.

✲ ✲ ✲ ✲ ✲

Personal Diary
Hannah Crawley
1 October 1851

Once I read a terrible story in an old book. A lady took a great fancy to a young wolf, or a bear, I forget which – but a bear, or a wolf, I believe it was. It had been given to her as a gift when still a cub. She was kind to it, for it was kind to her, and she treated it with great tenderness, and would play with it without fear or apprehension of danger, and it was obedient to all her commands, and its tameness, as she used to boast, increased with its growth; so that, like a lap-dog, it would follow her all over the house. But mind what followed: at last, somehow having disobliged it, it suddenly fell upon her, and devoured her. And who was most to blame? The beast, or the lady? Surely it was the lady to blame. For all the bear did was follow its own nature.

I am ruined, sure as that lady – and sure as that lady it is my own fault. Oh, why did I let him –?

Ah! I can write no more of this nonsense to myself. I shall put my papers and letters in a little box, and put that box in a drawer, and lock that drawer with a key. The key I shall keep. Some time hence when all this is over, and I can better bear to read them, I may take that key and open that drawer and take up that box and retrieve my papers. I shall preserve them, for we often look back with pleasure even upon the heaviest griefs, when the cause of them is removed. In this way shall I retain some hope for happier days to come.

✲ ✲ ✲ ✲ ✲

Ship's Log
Taylor writing
2 October 1851

The weather continues cold and raw, with some snow and strong northwesterly winds. Along with our fateful iceberg, winter appears to have arrived. Our men are variously employed collecting driftwood along the beach (the availability of which is itself an improvement over our last winter) for the distance of several miles. Others are occupied collecting stones from the neighbouring hills and stacking them on the beach for ballast, that they might be made available for the following season. The men now refer to our location by the name of Ballast Beach. The river south they call Maxwell's Way.

We have taken our seasonal survey of the stores. Excepting some small damage done by the remaining damp in the bread room, formerly mentioned, the only important discovery was a strange loss of candles. We had not properly secured the storeroom in question, and it seems an Arctic fox or some other creature such as a lemming has slipped in unobserved and opened some of the boxes and devoured the contents. This is not a dangerous loss, but inconvenient in the extreme, given the approaching months of darkness. Perhaps if we can manage to shoot a few of the slippery seals, we can render the blubber for more lamp oil.

We still continue our shooting and exploring expeditions with much eagerness and better success than our last overwintering gave us reason to hope. Ptarmigan frequently reward our labours. A beautiful specimen of a falcon was shot this morning when flying over the ship. Yesterday, a bear and two cubs were observed from the ship, on the ice, coming towards the shore; after wandering about on the floe for a short time sniffing the air in their usual style, they sagaciously betook themselves to flight, and spoiled our anticipated sport. A black fox was also seen by one of our men, on the land (the first of that species we had met with), but which fled at the report of his gun when firing at a small pack of ptarmigan.

✲ ✲ ✲ ✲ ✲

2 October 1851

TO: Vice Admiral Joseph Baring
British Navy
London Office

Baring,

What news from the whalers? Has any word of the expedition reached you through the usual channels? I understand your hesitance to pose outright questions to your associates. Your interest in the endeavour remains – and shall remain – a matter of utmost secrecy. And yet, I beg you to remember that my son is aboard, and that I have not heard tidings of him in over a year. If, by any means, you are able to exert your influence to obtain information from ships or traders in the Arctic region, please, for the love of God, I ask you to do so. He has been a poor, unwilling son to me, but he is my blood and I would have him safe.

My thoughts misgive me, Joseph. Did I do wrong, to send him?

Yours &c.

Sir Francis
Ashfield Manor
Caterham on the Hill, Surrey

* * * * *

Overland Expedition Log
Resumed
3 October 1851

Hall has made careful study of all the bones and bodies we found. Several, he was able to identify by some arcane physical detail, but others were too far – destroyed – to be identifiable. I bade him reconstruct these men, as best he is able, that they may be buried with as much human dignity as possible. Mackenzie, he identified by the characteristic torus fracture of his right arm: common, apparently, in ship carpenters. The boy, Charles, was easier to identify, his smaller body obvious even to me. Several others were nothing more than piles of anonymous bone: to this, we are all reduced, I know – but it is profane to see it. Caulderson, we think, is not here. Hall is confident he would have been able to identify his body based upon the information I provided him as to broken bones, etc. Further, his signet ring – which he never removed, ever – is not here. He must be one of the three who are unaccounted for, and this provides me some relief. We sorted the grisly relics as best we could, and interred them with an awful solemnity. I recited the Prayer for the Dead and we sang a hymn.

⁂ ⁂ ⁂ ⁂ ⁂

Captain's Log
3 October 1851

Thank God! Thank God, he is not here. The horror of believing him here, of imagining him as witness to this! And thinking of his terrible end! I feel as though I can breathe again, and only hope that he has not been consigned to some worse fate.

I have had reason before, and no doubt I will have again, to thank God for Embleton Hall.

⁂ ⁂ ⁂ ⁂ ⁂

Overland Expedition Log
Resumed
4 October 1851

We have tarried too long in this terrible place, and must now to action. The land is cold – frozen almost to iron hardness. Thompson turned his ankle digging the third shallow grave with his inadequate trowel. He cannot walk, but hobbles, instead, with a make-shift crutch. His ankle is swollen to more than twice its usual size, so that he can barely get his boot on. It is a danger for frostbite and gangrene if I have ever seen one. I have determined to send him and Sugden back to the ship, while Hall and I carry on in search of the three remaining *Vanguard* men. We will move faster this way, for while they are strong, we are quick and nimble, and we consume less. We shall take the small tent, sending the larger back with them. We have blankets and slops, some provisions, and rifles and ammunition. We should not stand a chance of surviving winter exposure out on the ice, but here, inland, our odds are much better. We are in agreement: we must go on.

5 October 1851

Thompson and Sugden departed north at 06:00, and only upon my direct orders and over their strenuous protest. We left shortly after, and how glad we were to put that terrible place, with its air of brutality and desperation, far behind us. With just the two of us, we gained nearly fifteen miles on this day's journey, in spite of a strong cold wind and constant snow. Hall sees signs that men have passed this way before us.

6 October 1851

After starting at 06:00, we proceeded in spite of a very cold fall of snow, until almost 20:00. Carrying my rifle, I shot three ptarmigan over the course of the day, and saw a white fox, but did not kill it. We must now melt snow to drink, and carry our flasks under our slops to keep them from freezing. With wood plentiful, however, we are able to build a small fire at night, which adds greatly to our comfort as well as being the means by which we cook our fowl. We are not quite so desperate, yet, as to eat raw flesh. Ah, I cannot write such a thing now without a shudder of revulsion.

7 October 1851

Today we passed several low points and islands of limestone. The sun had a great effect on the snow, and the aspect of the land was hourly changing. The last part of our journey was unusually laborious because of wedged masses of ice along the riverbed, so packed as to denote the great violence which they had undergone in the sudden freezing; but we at length passed them all, and encamped. Hall tells me that at noon the thermometer was at 47°, and at midnight at 32°. He somehow contrived to snare a pair of lemmings today; they were unpleasant to eat. I write this in the tent as hailstones pound around us. I pray the tent is not damaged.

8 October 1851

We encountered another obstacle today: thick ice pressed up to the precipices along the riverbank, and we were often obliged to quit a tolerable track to get round them in the best manner that we could. But the labour kept us warm and we made 11 miles. We pitched by 19:30, spending an hour or so in quiet conversation.

⁂ ⁂ ⁂ ⁂ ⁂

9 October 1851

TO: Mrs. Addie Maxwell
#3 West Hill Place
Brighton

Dear Mrs. Maxwell,

I trust you will excuse the intrusion of this letter. We are not ourselves acquainted, but share a common acquaintance in one Miss Hannah Crawley, from whom I received your address to write, in my capacity as her physician.

Perhaps you have heard about her recent change in circumstances with the death of Mr. Crawley? What you will not have heard, I suspect, is the grave financial state in which the man has left her. In short: Miss Crawley is near destitute, and very ill. Her father has left her nothing but a mountain of debt. She does not even own the house, for it had been promised to Worthington's upon his death as security against a large loan, and she must be out within a fortnight. Believe me when I say that the circumstances of this transaction were quite sordid, and he was lucky that the details did not reach the press.

Miss Crawley requires absolute rest. I fear she is on the verge of complete nervous collapse, and any further strain on her will be calamitous.

She has asked me to write you, not being equal to the task herself, to beg your indulgence and kindness. Would you, perhaps, take her in for a month or two? I would do it myself, in an instant, but I have no wife and such an arrangement would not be seemly. In my medical opinion, a month at the seaside would do the girl a world of good.

One word of caution, however: I have often seen your name in the newspapers in association with a certain political organization now active in agitating for particular social reforms quite distasteful to the public at large. I must beg and instruct you not to discuss such matters with Miss Crawley, nor to expose her to their proponents. She is a gentle girl, most retiring and admirably meek in her ways. Propagandizing would not be conducive to her wellbeing – not now, and not in the long term. She has been forced to endure enough misdirected passion in her life, and now requires only quiet rest and easy contemplation. If you can abide by this request, I believe we shall get on quite well. If not, I shall make other arrangements for her care. On this point I am firm.

I enclose payment here for her room and board, and will bring her up by private carriage if you are amenable.

Yours &c.,

Dr. Barnabas Brown
#9 Harley Street
London

✿ ✿ ✿ ✿ ✿

Naturalist's Log
8 October 1851

I confess that I am struggling to maintain proper scientific rigour and discipline – even regular logging of activities and observations. This is the most physically difficult period I have endured in my life, and I include in that estimation my first weeks aboard *Serapis*. It is not the march itself that is difficult, nor the cold, which is not as extreme as we have experienced heretofore. It is the relentless, monotonous *grind* of it. I am a man who sprints, and this marathon wears at me dreadfully, body and mind. I am also very sore. Sore to my bones, and beginning to bruise in a way that has me digging through snowdrifts and hunting among frozen grasses for traces of last year's sorrel and coltsfoot when I should be snaring lemmings and rabbits. Perhaps my body is simply exhausted, or perhaps –

In any case, I believe our pursuit nears an end. I have been seeing increasing indications of human activity for several days, although I have not mentioned this fact to David. There is an Esquimeaux encampment ahead, I am sure of it: two or three days' journey, I estimate. If Caulderson has made it this far, he must be there – he and his two companions – unless he is buried somewhere in a drift of snow.

I should wish him dead, should I not? I certainly used to, for he was my rival in the only fight that has ever mattered in my life. But it is so different here. *I* am so different here. There is no fight, and there are no rivals. Caulderson is a good man, I know, or David – *my* David – would not love him. And so, I wish only – life. One must strive so mightily to preserve it. In this place, especially, I cannot wish otherwise.

Nights in our little tent are short, for we are asleep almost the instant we lie down, but these hard, cold, uncomfortable nights, curled together for warmth and comfort: they are also my happiest, for we are together. I would follow him to the ends of the earth – indeed, I suppose I have – for less than this.

Chapter Eight: October – December 1851

Aklaq speaks to her son after they depart the death camp at Kittigazuit:

Stories are powerful, and some are very dangerous, very frightening. You have to be careful who you tell them to, and when, and how. Do you know the tale of Igimarasugdjuqdjuaq? It was told to me by my mother's father, but it is older even than that. I have never told it before.

Igimarasugdjuqdjuaq was a very large and very strong man. He did many wrong things. He hurt his wife. He committed many murders and even ate the flesh of his victims after he cut them up with his knife. Once upon a time his sister-in-law came to visit his wife, but scarcely had she entered the hut before Igimarasugdjuqdjuaq killed her and commanded his wife to cook her.

His wife was very much frightened, fearing that she herself would be the next victim, and resolved to escape. When Igimarasugdjuqdjuaq left to go hunting, she gathered heather, stuffed her clothing with it, and made a figure. She placed this sitting on the bed. Then she ran away as fast as she could and succeeded in reaching her father's village. When her husband came home and saw the figure, he believed that it was a stranger who had come to visit him and stabbed it. When he discovered, however, that his wife had deceived him, he fell into a passion and pursued her.

He came to the village and said, "Have you seen my wife? She has run away." The Inuit did not tell him that she had fled to them, but concealed her from his wrath. At last Igimarasugdjuqdjuaq gave her up for lost and returned home.

The Inuit, however, resolved to revenge the many outrages which he had wrought. They went to visit him and met him on the ice just below his hut. When he told them he was going bear hunting, they said, "Let us see your spear." This spear had a stout and sharp walrus tusk for a point. "Ah," said they, "that is good for bear hunting; how sharp it is. You must hit him just this way." And so saying, they struck his brow, the point of the spear entering his brain. Then they cut the body up with their knives and scattered it in four directions.

This is the law: once you have eaten human meat, you can never return to the dwellings of men. This must be the law for Inuit and qallunaat alike.

✲ ✲ ✲ ✲ ✲

Ship's Log
Lew Taylor writing
9 October 1851

I have determined that the usual winter preparations of housing in and snowing the upper deck should be deferred for another two or three weeks, with a view of economizing the lights which are becoming scarce, our provisions of both lamp oil and candles now sorely depleted. When daylight is no longer available and the true Arctic winter begins, we shall hastily complete these operations – with any luck, for the final time. Temperatures below deck are thus colder than usual, and below what we would expect for comfort's sake. For coal, we are limited to eight to twelve lbs per day, and see that they are carefully burned in those periods of the day in which it is most necessary to have a fire. The men have taken to sleeping in doubled woolen layers.

From this date, I have placed the men on half rations from ship's stores, which consist of four-and-a-half ounces of vegetables daily, ten ounces of meat daily (but making due allowance for bone in the salt, and jelly in the fresh meat, the average weight does not exceed eight ounces), and a further twelve ounces of flour for hardtack. Tea, cocoa and sugar are issued by the half ounce, although full rations of rum still remain. Carruthers protests that this allowance is quite inadequate to maintain health for any lengthy period, particularly when exposed to the rigorous severity of intense cold; however, game remains plentiful enough. We may be hungry, but as long as we can hunt, we will not starve.

It only remains for us, therefore, to bear with patience and fortitude the privations inseparable from our situation, to hope for strength and courage to meet and overcome those still greater which may await us, and to carry out our duties with all zeal and energy. We trust that the rescue party will return to us shortly, and that they will bring good tidings of the *Vanguard* survivors.

We cannot light the exterior of the ship indefinitely in the ever-lengthening darkness, but continue to sound off guns every hour through the long night, and trust this will be sufficient to guide them home to us.

✲ ✲ ✲ ✲ ✲

Overland Expedition Log
Resumed
Recorded by Captain David Maxwell
10 October 1851

We continue on. Hall believes he has seen signs of past human activity in the area, but thus far we have found no men, European or Esquimeaux. Hall is a most observant tracker – truly, the best I have seen. If anyone can find Caulderson and his remaining men, it is surely him.

* * * * *

Captain's Log
10 October 1851

We must be close – very close. And yet, the suspense, for me, is gone. I walk towards the inevitable, and whatever we find, we shall find. I have been numb for days now: since the death camp, I believe. It is the cold, but it is more than that. The circumstances of my life have habituated me to feeling and not speaking. Now – I feel nothing whatsoever.

* * * * *

Ship's Log
Taylor writing
10 October 1851

I've ordered every man who can hold a gun out to shore daily in search of game; today a deer was shot, and a number of ptarmigan. The men have full permission to eat immediately half of what they kill, provided they distribute it equally amongst themselves. The other half is laid on for winter. I have sent a three-man party out northeast onto the ice in search of seals: for a quantity of seal blubber, rendered down to oil, would provide excellent fuel for our lamps and help to stave off the coming darkness for a few more days or weeks. This could make an immeasurable difference to the crew's morale this winter. The party has taken a large sledge and provisions for a week, but I cannot estimate the likelihood of their success, for our luck with seals has never been great.

In summer we endure many difficulties and privations while hunting in the Arctic. When days are short and twilight reigns, these greatly increase. Often, true night falls while we are still at the chase, and the land is shrouded in darkness – moon and starlight alone enabling us faintly to discern the outline of the object of which we are in eager and anxious pursuit.

* * * * *

10 October 1851

TO: Mr. Christopher Foster, Solicitor
317 White Oaks, London

Dear Sir,

I have not troubled you for several years, and I have no doubt you will be surprised to hear from me now.

However, a situation has arisen that requires a significant financial outlay on my part. I wish to draw upon the interest, and indeed a portion of the capital, of my current investment with your firm. You shall try to talk me out of it, no doubt, and I shall refuse, so let us omit that portion of the conversation entirely. I expect you follow my directions exactly. I will call upon you early in the day on 14 October to give my instructions.

Sincerely,

Dr. Barnabas Brown
#9 Harley Street
London

* * * * *

Surgeon's Log
10 October 1852

As winter's cold and dark again approach, the spectre of scurvy raises its head once more. Our fresh sorrel leaves provided excellent relief during the brief months of summer, but it lies not in my power to provide the necessary amounts – or even a full diet – to the men now in my care.

Whether or not the small quantity of leaves I was able to dry will have a salubrious effect, I cannot say, but regardless, there is not enough to see us through a month, let alone an entire winter. So scanty is the remaining lime, that I can only give it in the most sparing quantity, and cannot continue its administration sufficiently long to be permanently beneficial – merely allaying the more urgent scorbutic symptoms in a few of the men most affected. Even with a more liberal supply, it would be next to an impossibility to eradicate the disease entirely, the cause of disease still being present. I fully expect the scurvy to be worse this winter and, I fear, more deadly – for although the men recovered reasonably well over the course of the summer, yet they are not as well as they could be, and we begin the difficult season in worse general health.

* * * * *

Overland Expedition Log
Recorded by Captain David Maxwell
11 October 1851

It was almost 18:00 today, the world in twilight, when we came upon two snow huts – igloos, as the Esquimeax call them – built up perhaps 20 or 30 yards from the edge of the tributary. They had tumbled in upon themselves during the brief summer melt, but enough of the structures remained that they were identifiable as dwellings. Still, covered as they are now with fresh snow, I would have missed their presence altogether, so much did they look like simple snowbanks, but Hall's keen eye identified them almost upon first sight. We called out, and were met with only an eerie silence.

Upon further investigation of the settlement, we discovered evidence of terrible violence. In the remains of one snow hut were the frozen and horribly mutilated bodies of four persons, all savages: two children (one little more than an infant), a woman, and an elderly man. In regards to what has happened to them, we do not yet know.

In the other hut, two European sailors lay side by side, as if sleeping, their throats cut down to the bone. Caulderson himself was nowhere to be seen – dead or alive.

We do not know what has happened. Beside the bodies was a pile of clothing, from undergarments to slops. Even boots were there. We discovered the appended letter under this clothing, folded around a signet ring.

* * * * *

May 1851 – I believe it to be May but am not certain.

I have done it. I have done the needful thing. Perhaps it was also the just thing; I cannot say, for justice is very distant now. I only know that it was needful. I thought –

Hang the Empire. It is all lies. We are no more than animals: rutting and gorging and killing in our viciousness, in our madness. I understand. I see clearly. Like poorly-trained dogs, when our master turns his back, we revert to our true natures. The instant I departed to hunt, my men –

There is only one remedy for a mad dog. I have carried out that remedy as my principles required, but I sicken with it, with our corruption. I am the commander, and I am responsible. Their actions are mine. The children! My God, what they did to the children.

Complete and utter erasure – this is now my only wish. I am in the one place on this planet where such a thing may actually be effected. This fact, and only this, allows me to retain any faith in the goodness of God. I shall let the ice take me, and then William Caulderson and his whole damned expedition will be no more.

Those who are too sick to live in the world without harming it must be wise enough, and brave enough, to face up to self-slaughter. I am sorry. Good bye. God bless you. I shall see it through.

William Caulderson, Captain.

⚬ ⚬ ⚬ ⚬ ⚬

Naturalist's Log
11 October 1851

I did what I could to shield him from the worst of it, but by God – it was very bad.

I saw the ruined igloos long before he did, of course, and sought to investigate them before he could notice my activity. I do not wish to conceal truths from him, but I would soften them, if I could. The first was – it was a bloodbath, imperfectly preserved in the changing weather, and all the more terrible for that. I did not take the time to investigate fully, for David was approaching and I wished to prevent him from coming closer. Something frightful happened here.

"Several Esquimeaux are dead," I said only. "David – there are children. There is nothing we can do now for them."

"And in the other?" he asked. He seemed strangely blank.

I conducted a cursory examination of the second structure while he watched from a distance, and returned to him a few moments later with the letter.

"Caulderson is not here," I said immediately. He made no reaction.

I handed him the letter and the ring. "There are two dead sailors, but Caulderson is not among them."

I watched him closely as he read the letter. His strange and unnatural calm worries me greatly.

He read the letter through once, and then read it aloud for my benefit, still betraying no emotion. His face, though, was very pale.

"What –" he paused to clear his throat. "What did he do?" He looked at me with such blankness, such complete apathy, that I was chilled.

"He killed them, David. He killed his men." I tried to be gentle.

He nodded. "And the others? The Esquimeaux?"

I shrugged. "They were also killed, but I cannot say by whom. We can extrapolate from the letter that –"

David shook his head. "They wouldn't. British sailors – *his* men – wouldn't slaughter innocent civilians. Not even savages. Not – not children."

I said nothing, but he must have read my thoughts on my face: when death knocks, men become brutal and unpredictable.

"They wouldn't, Em," he said again. I almost wished he would be angry with me, then, but his voice was flat and his eyes were empty.

David went, then, and examined both igloos while I walked up another hundred yards and pitched our tent for the night. I gathered brushwood and built a small fire. After a while, when David had still not come, I made tea – two cups, with all of our remaining sugar in his – and went in search of him. He was standing between the two igloos, that same blank look still on his face. I handed him his tea, which he took and drank without a word. I saw that he had slipped Caulderson's ring onto his own finger.

"In the morning, we can start our search for the – for Caulderson," I said. Having left his clothing, his body must be nearby. "I can track him. We will discover him and properly bury him."

"No," David said, finally looking at me. "No. We must honour his final wish. He is gone, Embleton. They are all gone."

He let me take his arm, then, and lead him back to our camp. All the time, he worried at the ring on his hand.

He ate a little when I put food before him, and lay at my side in silence all through the night. I do not know if he slept. I certainly did not.

* * * * *

Naturalist's Log
12 October 1851

It was not a restful night, but we rose at 05:00 and by mutual agreement began to search out stones – a task made difficult by the darkness of the season. We cannot bury the dead; David insists that we honour Caulderson's final wish. But we must somehow mark this place, even if we are the only men to ever see it. I also took the opportunity to snare an Arctic hare. I must force David to eat.

We finished the cairn at 17:30. It stands between the two igloos, which we covered over with more snow.

We stood together, when it was finished, and I waited for David to perform his office and speak the Prayer for the Dead or some other words. After a time, I glanced at him. He was staring at the cairn with a face devoid of any emotion, eyes both dry and dead.

I did not know what to do. I could pray.

"Toll for the Brave!" I quoted finally. "The Brave that are no more."

He nodded, once, and that was the end of it.

❊ ❊ ❊ ❊ ❊

Kingmiatook, who escaped with one child, speaks of the terrible deeds of the mad qallunaat:

At this time we had built our two iglus on the west side of Anjikuni. We were there to hunt the earliest spring deer at Kivalliq as they came down through Kazan River. When the qallunaat came, the strongest men, Siluk and Tukkuttok, were out hunting. We wives, Qannik and I, we and our children, and one elder too old to keep up with the young men, were left in camp. At that time, the three qallunaat came to the camp. When they entered the camp, all the Inuit were inside one of the iglus; we started hearing voices outside. Little Qannik, Siluk's second wife, said,

"The hunters are here – they're back already." We didn't expect them for many days yet. She went out to see them, but she came back very shaky and said, "They're not Inuit; they're not human." Everyone got scared, very, very scared, and no one wanted to go outside.

But the old man, Eqilaglu, when he heard something outside the iglu, he went out to investigate. When he saw what was there, he said to himself, "No, I have never seen anything like this."

He said, "I've never in my life seen a devil or a spirit. I am not annatko. If things are not human, I cannot see them. I have never in all my life seen any kind of spirit – I've heard the sounds they make, but I've never seen them with my own eyes. I can see these creatures. Therefore these are not spirits."

Eqilaglu went over to touch one, to feel if it was cold or warm. He had thought to himself, "If they are human, I can feel them. If they are human, they will be warm. If devils or spirits, they will have no heat." So he touched a cheek with his hand: it was cool, but not as cold as a fish. They were beings, but not Inuit. They were beings, but he didn't know what they were.

These beings seemed disoriented – not interested in us, more aware of the iglu building; touching it. The old man invited them inside and we women tried to give them something to eat: seal meat that was cut up small, and we gave them water to drink. The beings drank the water. But when we tried to give them seal meat, they'd take a bite and then spit it out. We gave them soup, and they took a little of that.

Eqilaglu instructed us to bring these beings to the other iglu – the empty one. They did not seem dangerous but they were palakhonguliqtut – getting weak, weak from hunger – and they seemed very strange. They fell asleep in their iglu.

After a long, long time, one of the beings came out of the iglu and called to us in strange words that we could not understand. The old man was sleeping now, but I went out with Osha asleep on my back because I was less afraid than Qaanik.

The being made it known to me with motions of his hands that he wanted water, which I gave to him. He showed me with his body that he was cold, and pointed that the others were cold, too. In this way, we learned that they were men like us, and that they could feel the cold.

I bid him wait, and returned to the iglu. We talked it over for a long time: what best to do with these strange men. I did not think they were strong enough to hurt us, even if they wanted to, but Qannik was still affected by the shock of first seeing them, and was afraid for the children, and for herself. In the end, we decided to bring them into our warm iglu, where we could watch over them and observe their actions.

This was not a right decision. I am sorry for what came.

✲ ✲ ✲ ✲ ✲

Overland Expedition Log
Resumed
Naturalist Embleton Hall writing
13 October 1851

I assume log duties at the behest of Captain Maxwell, whose right hand has sustained a moderate frostbite during yesterday's labours. I have warmed and wrapped it; he shall recover fully with time, but use of it is now too painful to permit sustained writing.

Our mission now complete, we must hasten back to the *Serapis* before true winter falls. The time is short. Our present object is to proceed a minimal distance of 35 miles each day, not pausing at sun-fall, nor pausing to hunt except when absolutely necessary. Our small stock of provisions will see us through, though not, certainly, in comfort. We shall rest and recharge our energies when we reach the food cache deposited by Taylor's party – in perhaps twenty days' time. Possibly we shall even overtake Thompson and Sugden, and carry on together.

* * * * *

Kingmiatook, who escaped with one child, tells how it ended:

The strange beings were very weak; their behaviour made little sense to us. The one who seemed to be the leader slept a great deal and would take little food. When Osha began to fuss and I took her to my breast, he opened his eyes and smiled and spoke some words in his strange tongue before he slept again, but I do not know what he said.

The other two strange beings slept less; they were restless and noisy. They took food: so much that they became ill on it and vomited up over the skin floor. Then they shouted and frightened the children, and Osha began to fuss again. One grabbed Qannik's arm as she knelt to clean the mess. He pulled her to himself and put his hands on her in ways she did not like.

The leader man spoke sharply, then, and he released her, but we women saw and understood: we saw what kind of man this was.

It was not long after that the three beings removed themselves to the other iglu, taking a skin of water and a little meat with them. They were noisy amongst themselves; their black lips were cracked and terrible and their voices loud long into the night. Much later, the leader came again to our iglu. He had a number of items with him: a sack and a long branch-that-was-not-a-branch, and other things. He spoke some words, and then he was gone.

Eqilaglu said he thought the man had gone hunting; or maybe he had gone to fetch help for his companions. We did not know, because there are no other beings like this in the land, but it was an interesting thing to talk about it. In the end, we decided he must be hunting. We thought he was likely to return within a day or two. He did not seem strong enough for a longer expedition.

The two beings left in the other iglu were quiet for a time, and we thought they were asleep, or maybe dead. When we slept, we were uneasy. We did not understand the strange feeling that had entered our camp.

We woke to find the two beings standing in our midst. One was digging through the frozen stores of meat; the other was piling all of Qannik's good skins into a sack on his back. We watched and waited to see what would happen next.

The beings ransacked everything, and piled up all our best meat and skins, my bone needles from my mother, the soft breeches I am making for Tukkuttok. All the while they shouted and laughed and made ugly sounds. The children were frightened, but they knew to be silent – even Osha.

They took turns hauling the skins and meat back to the other iglu. One would go out with an armful of goods, and the other would stand at the entrance, watching us.

After a long time of this, all the skins and meat and cooking utensils were gone from our iglu. Even the floor skin was gone, and we were sitting on snow. One of the beings came to me an pulled off my amauti. The other being laughed and moved to Qannik. He took up her amauti and pulled off her boots, tossing them all outside. I thought he would go, then, to take them back to the other iglu, leaving us naked to freeze or starve.

But he made ugly sounds in his throat. He unfastened his own clothing and pushed Qannik down onto the ground. She pushed him off. The other being laughed.

Then things began to happen very slowly, and also very quickly.

The being on top of Qannik slapped her face. Her children, the little one and the big girl, began to cry.

Then Eqilaglu rose up. I believe the beings had forgotten about him until that moment. He rose up then, and said "No. You must stop this." He put power into his words.

But the being by the door came at him with a long, terrible knife. He stabbed him in the belly, as if he were gutting him; as if he were prey. Qannik's big girl cried out and ran to Eqilaglu, she tried to ease him down onto the ground. The terrible being kicked the child, and she fell away, senseless.

Then Qannik began to fight, and she had the spirit of the mother white bear: biting and clawing at the being on top of her until he rolled away, and she pulled her little ulu from its place by the wall and slashed at his face, and so we learned that the beings bleed just as Inuit do.

Both beings howled in rage, and attacked in earnest, then, each with their long knives. There was much blood spilled, and they did not spare the children in their fury.

The blood from her many wounds ran out onto the snow, and as she died Qannik uttered the word "Pamiuluq!" That is the old, old language. Pamiuluq is a spirit with a bad tail. "Pamiuluq," she said as she died, calling on the Spirit to destroy these beings.

I took Osha to my breast and bid her be silent. I ran. I – a naked, unarmed woman – could do nothing else. The terrible beings were too engrossed in their killings to pay me mind. Even now, I cannot say whether they were men or tupilaq. It does not matter.

As I left the iglu, I stumbled upon Qannik's boots and amauti. I pulled them on as I ran, and slipped Osha into place on my back.

I ran until I could be sure the beings were not tracking me. I walked even longer after that, until Osha started to cry and I brought her forward to nurse. We walked for two days, and then we found Siluk and Tukkuttok and we were safe.

✲ ✲ ✲ ✲ ✲

Overland Expedition Log
Resumed
E. Hall writing
15 October 1851

Today we passed the cairn we erected at the place where our little tributary branched off from the main river south, on 28 September. Though the temperature is unpleasantly low, it is clear and calm, and our pace has been excellent. Neither of us wishes to stop, even when we are asleep on our feet. I do not recall if we stopped properly last night.

✲ ✲ ✲ ✲ ✲

Naturalist's Log
15 October 1851

Both very tired now. Very tired. He is not broken, I do not think. But he is – very quiet. He will tell me nothing of what goes on in his mind, and at night he is different. He will have me, but he will not speak to me, nor properly embrace me. I wish him to take what he needs from me; I only –

✲ ✲ ✲ ✲ ✲

15 October 1851

TO: Barclay, Bevan, and Co.
54 Lombard Street
London

Dear Sirs,

Enclosed please find a banker's draught in the amount of £747 to discharge the debt of Mr. Michael Crawley, deceased. We now consider the matter resolved and request that you desist in all communication with Miss H. Crawley. Any further business may be referred directly to this office.

Mr. Christopher Foster, Solicitor
317 White Oaks
London

* * * * *

15 October 1851

TO: Williams & Co.
20 Birchin Lane
London

Dear Sirs,

Enclosed please find a banker's draught in the amount of £1797 to discharge the debt of Mr. Michael Crawley, deceased. We now consider the matter resolved and request that you desist in all communication with Miss H. Crawley. Any further business may be referred directly to this office.

Mr. Christopher Foster, Solicitor
317 White Oaks
London

* * * * *

15 October 1851

TO: Merchant Bkg. Co.
112 Cannon St.
London

Dear Sirs,

Enclosed please find a banker's draught in the amount of £132 to discharge the debt of Mr. Michael Crawley, deceased. We now consider the matter resolved and request that you desist in all communication with Miss H. Crawley. Any further business may be referred directly to this office.

Mr. Christopher Foster, Solicitor
317 White Oaks
London

* * * * *

15 October 1851

TO: Martin and Co.
68 Lombard St.

Dear Sirs,

Enclosed please find a banker's draught in the amount of £487 to discharge the debt of Mr. Michael Crawley, deceased. We now consider the matter resolved and request that you desist in all communication with Miss H. Crawley. Any further business may be referred directly to this office.

Mr. Christopher Foster, Solicitor
317 White Oaks
London

⁂ ⁂ ⁂ ⁂ ⁂

Ship's Log
Taylor writing
16 October 1851

Warde and I bagged two deer today, both just a mile or so inland, and hauled them back to the ship on sledges. I had Smith immediately cook up a large portion for every man aboard to consume at once; the hot meal did wonders for morale – at least in the short term – reminding us that we are civilized men, after all, and not savages, feasting on raw flesh. I then ordered an extra hour of lamplight, and we passed an almost-pleasant evening.

No sight yet of the rescue party's return. We continue our hourly signals. Publicly, I maintain a façade of optimism and good cheer, but privately I have grave misgivings.

⁂ ⁂ ⁂ ⁂ ⁂

Overland Expedition Log
Resumed
E. Hall writing
16 October 1851

Up this morning at 05:00, and made five or six hours progress – perhaps ten miles. It then began to blow so hard, with drift snow, that we were obliged to halt for fear of losing our way in the storm. We built a make-shift snow wall to shelter our tent, the internal temperature of which did not rise above minus 5° the whole of the day.

Degrees of a thermometer make little impression on those who have not experienced true cold; and, above all, the minus side of the scale is meaningless to those who have not lived in lands like this. In this extremity, we sleep but little, passing our time instead in a sort of near-catatonia induced by the relentless howl of the wind and the persistence of the dark. We are nearly out of fuel for the spirit lamp, and dare not waste the little we have remaining for the luxury of light.

Despite the cold, it is good to rest. We need it.

19 October 1851

I deem it unnecessary to give a daily account of our trek, as our days are identical and my energies limited. We begin our march early, often in spite of a chilling wind, sometimes accompanied by snow. We press on as quickly as we can, stopping little. At 20:00, rarely earlier, we call halt and pitch for the night. If we are lucky enough to have meat in our packs (for I sometimes still manage a lemming or a hare) it is so hard frozen that we are obliged to cut it with a saw, and can only afford to thaw it by putting it into our warm tea: we cannot spare fuel for both purposes.

20 October 1851

We are no longer surprised to come upon bodies on this terrible, deathly trek. Death seems the most natural thing in the world, and life an unreasonable expectation. Mid-day today we stumbled upon the bodies of poor Peter Thompson and Hank Sugden. They were sitting side by side in a snowbank, looking for all the world as if they had sat down to rest, and simply never risen again. Thompson's boot was off, his entire leg from the knee down black with gangrene. We lack the strength to bury them, and even to build a cairn, but we covered them with snow, and stood over them a spell. We shall name this tributary after them.

We were obliged to leave most of their belongings with them where they lay, for we cannot carry more than we currently do. I took Peter's watch for his wife. Hank had nothing on his person worth preserving. We took a small amount of spirit fuel and several ship's biscuits and carried on.

23 October 1851

Imprisoned all yesterday by a storm, the path so difficult that we did not gain more than 300 yards in two hours before we decided to halt.

26 October 1851

It is said that there is no jesting with a hungry stomach; there is assuredly none in our case. Heaven only knows what will be our fate, should the animals of this country, with four legs or two, have plundered Taylor's food cache. Our strength begins to fail. Yet we press on.

28 October 1851

We could not proceed yesterday, in consequence of another gale. We can be no more than two or three days' walk from the cache. This, now, is our only thought. What torment to be so close.

✲ ✲ ✲ ✲ ✲

Ship's Log
Taylor writing
28 October 1851

The effects of cold and hunger begin to be felt, as evidenced in the number of admissions to the sick list – more numerous than at any former period, Carruthers tells me – with diseases resulting from these causes.

The men are become dispirited, from feeling their own inability to make the same exertions they have formerly done. Even the fittest among us are not as vigorous as we were. Many therefore do not take the same active part in the hunting as heretofore, and some have almost ceased to take any part in it. The result is that we have had less fresh meat to supplement our rations than we might have had, and I may be forced to recalculate our ration allowance should this situation continue or worsen over the coming winter.

✲ ✲ ✲ ✲ ✲

Surgeon's Log
30 October 1851

There is a new and unexpected practice among the men which causes me much concern. The small daily ration of meat shrinks so much when boiled or cooked that it merely affords a few mouthfuls to each, and fails to satisfy the keen craving of the appetite. In consequence, the practice of eating meat raw – whether salt, preserved, fresh, or in a half-frozen state – has been almost universally adopted; and what under other circumstances would appear revolting, is now eaten and enjoyed with a degree of avidity and relish. It must be experienced to be fully understood.

I fear this may contribute much towards the deterioration of health, and to the further development of a scorbutic diathesis; but it goes on uninterruptedly whatever I say. The feeling which prompts the men to the adoption of the practice appears to be but little under the control of the will; and the natural repugnance to raw meat, once overcome, is not easy for hungry men to relinquish.

With what chagrin do I recall our earlier repugnance at this savage Esquimeaux practice.

Our quantity of oil is also very small, which only enables us to have lights at certain periods of the day. At other times, we have the option of either walking on deck, or sitting in the dark. We look back upon last winter – a winter of convivial conversations and books and Dickens – with much fondness from this darker, hungrier time.

✲ ✲ ✲ ✲ ✲

Inuit saying, oft retold

Life's greatest danger lies in the fact that man's food consists entirely of souls.

* * * * *

Overland Expedition Log
Resumed
Hall writing
1 November 1851

Have reached the cache left by Taylor and his advance party. Upon our approach, we found it to be occupied by a fox, which soon made its escape. Everything was as we left it, and as we were not less hungry than cold, having finished our last morsel at yesterday's breakfast, we tucked into a good meal: our first in many weeks.

We rest here for the night, and then push hard for the ship. With our new stores of food and fuel, the last leg of our journey should be eminently bearable, despite the fact that we are now in almost perpetual darkness. If the weather holds clear, we shall be back in our cozy cabins in a matter of days. How strange to think with fondness and longing on what I formerly considered my prison. How circumstances change us.

* * * * *

Ship's Log
Taylor writing
4 November 1851

The sun took his entire departure yesterday, and the *Serapis* is for the second time shrouded in a mantle of darkness, this time accompanied by a cheerlessness and gloom. Our chief occupation is the hunt; now become more than ever a matter of duty for all to engage in who are able. As our needs are urgent, our best energies are devoted to it.

We all eagerly await Captain Maxwell's return, but I most particularly. A ship cannot fare well in the absence of her commander, and I'd far rather toil beside my men than command them. We all begin to fear that the ship is too dark to attract the party's notice in the winter season, and that they may miss us in the darkness. We have no lamp oil to spare, nor candles, but torches we can make, and we can sound our guns, as well. They must be back soon, or I fear they will not be back at all.

23:45

Thank God! They have returned.

* * * * *

Ship's Log
Captain David Maxwell writing
5 November 1851

My rescue party today returned to the ship; I have once more assumed command. Mr. Taylor has performed admirably in my absence under difficult conditions, and shall be rewarded upon return to London.

I bring grievous news of both our party and of the party which we sought. The small group of men who survived the sinking of the *Vanguard* is all dead: they died of starvation and exposure on their march south. Some evidence of snow madness. We properly erected a cairn; map appended. Expedition logs appended.

Of our own rescue party, Hall and I are the only survivors. Peter Thompson died of gangrene after an injury to his ankle on the return march, and Hank Sugden of exposure as he sought to care for his comrade. Their bodies lie where they died along the tributary as marked on map. Recommend tributary be named in memory of their brave sacrifice.

⁂ ⁂ ⁂ ⁂ ⁂

Naturalist's Log
5 November 1851

With what unutterable relief did we espy the *Serapis* at last! I believe the weight of our exhaustion hit us forcibly then, for the last mile to the ship was perhaps the most difficult of the entire journey. Indeed, several times we had to pause, unable to take another step. Taylor was wise to set torches burning around the ship: it was by their light that we were brought home. By the time we were close enough to halloo to the men aboard ship, the lookouts had spotted us and come out onto the ice to assist us in our final steps.

It was a somber homecoming.

Dr. Carruthers and Taylor met us first, and seeing our sad faces and our lack of companions, belayed the crew's enthusiastic welcome.

"To my great cabin," David croaked, and they were the first words I had heard from his mouth in many days. "Taylor, Carruthers, if you would…?"

Taylor sent the boy ahead with coal to light a fire, and called for tea and meat to be brought to the captain's table.

Before long, we were all sitting together at table, snug and warm and full of good food. What a luxury did it seem: the candle! The brandy! It was bliss, and I sank into my good chair with great pleasure. Only when I looked at David did my pleasure wane, for his face remained as blank and dead as it had since our final discovery.

He cleared his throat when our meal was finished, and took a long swallow of his drink. "Mr. Hall," he asked, "please brief the others on the findings of the party."

I did so, providing detailed information about everything except that final scene in the igloos. I do not wish Caulderson's memory to be tarnished any more than David does – and after all, only we two have any notion of the truth.

"We found the remainder of the *Vanguard* survivors dead in the igloo," I concluded. "They succumbed to the elements." I felt David's eyes on me, and he nodded briefly.

Taylor blew out his breath. "It is not the ending we had hoped for," he said. "And yet, we can do nothing but raise our glasses to our brave and intrepid comrades, and to their noble commander. The loss is ours," he went on, standing and raising his glass. "The gain is his. He has died in service to the Empire – and that is the greatest victory."

And then, most terribly, I heard David Maxwell laugh. It was long and loud, but there was no mirth in it. Taylor and Carruthers looked at each other uncomfortably. "If this is victory, I confess I do not see it," David said at last.

Not five minutes later, he sent us out, bidding Taylor send in a bottle of whiskey and not disturb him for twelve hours, at the least.

✲ ✲ ✲ ✲ ✲

Ship's Log
7 November 1851

Since I was not present for overwintering preparations, I have this day conducted a thorough check on the state of the ship. She appears to be in fine shape, physically, although supplies are low as noted by Taylor in the log. Hunting continues to be of the utmost importance to our continued survival.

The state of morale on board is gloomy to a degree we have not yet seen. The sick bay is full of occupants, and Carruthers reports that even those well enough to keep to their duties display symptoms of dysentery and other exhausting diseases, from the effects of cold and hunger acting on debilitated and scorbutic bodies.

We must have more fresh meat, and the fattier the better. We may consider sending out a sealing party, but seals are difficult prey at this time of year; I must consult upon the matter with Taylor and Hall.

* * * * *

11 November 1851

TO: Abiah Higginbotham
37 Upper Hannover Street
Sheffield

Abiah,

Thank you for your letter, dear; it was lovely to see you, as well. You will come back soon, won't you? While the country is most salubrious for the health, it grows a little tedious without the excitement of periodic (and most welcome) interruptions.

Hannah also sends her regards. Your visit was so good for her. She is unused to any society at all, and a friendly but not overly familiar face cannot but be a balm to her.

She's a solemn little thing, isn't she? And yet, so utterly charming. She frets constantly about her affairs and her prospects, but I have suggested that she leave the post and ignore the world at large until she is substantially stronger in her mind; she is not yet well enough to make these weighty decisions. Of course, she is welcome to stay with me for as long as she wishes. She has been through the fires, poor thing, but we shall soon set her right again. We shall soon set each other right again, in fact.

Her rather overbearing doctor visits from London every week, accepting no pay, and bids her to rest quietly as much as possible until her strength returns. He has forbidden her books of any sort, but of course we simply put them away until he is gone. They provide a welcome distraction to her, and are in my view invaluable to her recovery.

It seems to me, Abiah, that when one has been harmed in some deep and psychic way, one might either turn outward, in rage, or inward, in sorrow. My path tends always to the former, and Hannah's – from what I have seen – to the latter. We are in this way pleasingly complementary and helpful to each other; at least, we have agreed to each do our best for the other. She calms me. And I, when she is better, will strive to shake her out of her lassitude, and stir her to action. How unexpectedly pleasant it is to have a companion. I had misgivings at the beginning, as you know, but our arrangement is now delightful to me. In her presence, some of the terrible violence of feeling that blighted me in London begins to dissipate.

I did not think it would. I did not believe it possible that such an extremity of – of grief, of rage – would ever let me go, once it had me in its grip. But now I have this little cottage, and I have this dear little friend who needs me, and who is needed in turn, and – a little happiness creeps back. It is sweeter, for being so unexpected.

And there, I have no other news to relate! Thanks to your care and concern, I have no project or Committee business on my hands. How retiring am I. What a very good and obedient girl! I shall write again when (or if) some occurrence – which is to say, *any* occurrence – demands it.

And now – the sun is peeping out from behind the heavy clouds and we go to walk the beach as is our daily habit.

Addie Maxwell
#3 West Hill Place
Brighton

⁂ ⁂ ⁂ ⁂ ⁂

Captain's Log
15 November 1851

Yesterday, the ship's company, experiencing the cravings of hunger with more severity than before, came on the quarter-deck in a body to ask for more food. I refused to accede to the general body of men, but agreed to increase rations for the sick-list, which Carruthers has long requested. We who are well must apply ourselves more avidly to the hunt.

I record this here, and not in the Ship's Log, because I do not blame the men and do not wish them to face recriminations when I turn over the log to Sir Francis in London.

I wish conditions were better, but God knows I am not the man to provide them.

⁂ ⁂ ⁂ ⁂ ⁂

Surgeon's Log
29 November 1851

Our expedition's fourth death occurred this morning – that of able seaman Jaimie Lucas, from dropsy supervening on an affliction of the heart of only nine days duration, a man of scorbutic habit; and the fifth, an hour later, was that of David Kerr, gunner's mate, who had been long suffering from scurvy and debility, on which general dropsy supervened.

This man was so debilitated when first brought before me that he could not stand without support. Dropsical diseases are now of very frequent occurrence, owing to the vitiated state of the blood, but most fortunately none is as far advanced as it was in the cases of Lucas and Kerr. We have thus several acts of mournful duty to perform, two deaths having taken place in the course of a single day.

These duties will not, however, suffice to excuse the men from their hunting expeditions, for nothing – not even temperatures of 65° below zero – will convince Captain Maxwell to call off the daily hunt. It is now a common circumstance to find a hunter return so benumbed and helpless as to be barely able to reach the ship, and with utterance so impaired, as to render his speech difficult to be understood.

It is a trying period. The decks are in a most uncomfortable state, as none feels disposed to take more exercise than that prescribed in the usual daily routine, which is curtailed by an hour from what it was last winter. The air below is of an unhealthy character and surcharged with moisture. The men are constantly complaining of the cold, which is not to be wondered at, considering the nature of the atmosphere surrounding them, in which they sit, sleep, and eat; the discomfort of which is only equaled by its insalubrity, as the sick list now but too fully proves.

Indeed, the transition of temperature from the lower to the upper deck, by merely walking up a few steps of a ladder, at times exceeds one hundred degrees. It, therefore, has become necessary to guard as much as possible against its evil effects, by wearing a fold of the netted woolen comforter over the mouth, in the form of a respirator. I have a Jeffrey's Respirator in use, and tested its efficacy in the coldest temperatures. I found that it considerably modified the irritating effects of the inhalation of cold air, until the accumulation of ice obstructed it. I can, therefore, strongly recommend it, as it enables me to allow invalids in the coldest weather such an amount of exercise as I deem it necessary for them to take.

⚬ ⚬ ⚬ ⚬ ⚬

Captain's Log
1 December 1851

I feel myself begin to despair, for this mission has been a failure from start to finish, and now more good men are dead because of me, and because of *him*.

It is only when I am alone with Embleton, now, when we lie together, silent and trembling, that I ever feel anything at all. And then: I am flayed open, to my heart, to my very bones, and it is too much and I do not know how to tell him the thousandth part of what I feel, and so I say nothing at all.

Man is an animal, unredeemed and unredeemable. I see it in myself, and in the men around me, gobbling their raw meat and huddling together for warmth. I sicken with the knowledge of our bestial nature. For if good men can degenerate into – into what the *Vanguard* men became, at their end – what hope can there be for any of us?

I miss my Addie profoundly, her strange knack for hearing all the words I cannot say and speaking back to me as if I had given them voice. I wonder where she is now.

⚬ ⚬ ⚬ ⚬ ⚬

Naturalist's Log
6 December 1851

Physically, we have recovered from our overland expedition. With better, more regular nutrition – even at the small rations now afforded us aboard ship – and with rest, we have regained much of the physical strength we lost. I believe I slept for more than two days upon our return.

David will not speak to me, even now. Or rather – he condescends, most unwillingly, to speak to me of things inconsequential, but will not say a word about his inner thoughts: that which I most value. I imagine he feels some guilt for the deaths we have suffered, for he is a most attentive and responsible commander. I imagine he grieves for Caulderson. Beyond that – well. I never can predict him.

There is at least the chase to keep him occupied, for I fear mental and physical stagnation would be disastrous for him just now. Our techniques must be adjusted, that much is clear to me. We cannot waste our time on the larger mammals: it is unlikely in the extreme that we will bring down a bear in this season, for example; or even, alternately, a seal.

We must swallow our pride and turn to the small mammals, and I must resume my study of their digestion and diet. Even the non-hibernating species must certainly undergo a metabolic shift to survive the harsh conditions, the study and documentation of which shall be my chief occupation in the coming months.

I made several observations during the overland expedition which may now prove useful to us in obtaining our daily meat.

1. That Foxes, Lemmings, and several species of birds all burrow in the snow for the sake of warmth.
2. That the Hares frequent some localities in considerable numbers, conveying the idea of their being at certain seasons gregarious, but that one small disturbance by Man is enough to send them fleeing for hours or days from these very localities.
3. That Lemmings and Mice are met with in vast numbers in virtually all regions thus far explored in the north.
4. That Lemmings and Mice subsist chiefly on the vegetable products of the soil – dwarf willow and the grasses, &c. – but they have likewise a carnivorous propensity, for I have frequently known them to eat each other.

I recall I once mocked the importance of *Mus musculus*. I shall certainly never do so again. But how to obtain them in sufficient quantities?

✲ ✲ ✲ ✲ ✲

Naturalist's Log
21 December 1851

Fitting, to be writing this entry on the darkest day of the year – what might have been the darkest day of my life.

I did not see David all day. I watched for him, as I always do, but he did not emerge from his cabin. I saw Taylor look for him as well, and I saw several men glance quizzically between him and Carruthers, clearly worried about their captain's wellbeing. It became apparent by 16:00 that he would not be making an appearance amongst the crew this day – an anomaly, but only just. He has, in truth, been more absent than present since our return, in both factual and figurative senses, and even I can see that the men feel it keenly.

I have attempted to distract them. They need their captain to truly rally their spirits, but in his absence – quite contrary to my own inclinations and habits – I do what I can to allay their worry and their boredom. I do it for his sake.

In the near-constant darkness, we rely upon the sharing of remembered stories and long-familiar tales, which we repeat to each other again and again. I find myself surprised by the number of novels, plays, and other trivial entertainments that have found their way into long-neglected corners of my mind. I have become quite popular, it shocks me to relate, for the number and quality of stories I am able to recall, and the detail with which I impart them.

I spent the afternoon in such pursuits, and for a time the men were, I flatter myself, transported from their dire present conditions.

After several hours, Josh Pine took over with an insipid retelling of *Einen Jux will er sich machen*, a play he clearly barely understood on his single, confused viewing, but an excellent opportunity for me to slip away, as the men were enthralled.

I went silently then to David's cabin, and rapped softly on the door.

There was no sound from within, but so uneasy was I about him that I easily forced the simple lock and entered.

I have never been so mortally shocked in my life.

He was sitting on the edge of his bunk, staring at a Colt revolver in his hand. For his part, he seemed unsurprised at my sudden appearance. He did not even look my way. I wanted to rush to him and wrench the terrible instrument from his hands, but I forced myself to be still.

"David?" I said. He made no reply, but I saw his hand twitch on the weapon. I took a step into the room, and then another, and closed the door softly behind me.

"Tell me, Embleton," he said, and his face was placid as a death mask, but his voice was rough with emotion. "Tell me how to bear it."

I took another step closer while he continued to speak. "He could not live with it, and he – he *made* me! So tell me: how can I bear it?"

I was almost close enough now to touch him. I had no idea what to say. How could I, broken and wretched as I am, give any man a reason to live – let alone a man such as he? But speak I must.

"Do you wish for comfort, or for truth?" I asked, for it seemed to me imperative to know which strategy might have best effect.

He choked out an ugly little laugh. "I wish for both."

He asks the impossible of me with bewildering regularity.

Now that I had engaged him in conversation, I felt it safe to advance further into the cabin. I lowered myself to sit on the bunk beside him; the warmth of his body against my shoulder gave me succor. We were silent for long moments. I decided I must speak only of what I know, for I would not patronize David Maxwell, of all men.

"I am a naturalist and an atheist," I said. "I do not claim to be a good man, but rather, an empirical man, a scientist. I derive the things I know to be true from the careful and systematic observation of the world around me. And I can tell you honestly that Caulderson's analysis was incomplete, coloured by the singular circumstances of his most unusual life."

David had turned to look at me, and so I continued. "We men are physical, material creatures: a complex, highly organized collection of muscles, tissues, organs, bone, acted upon by circumstance. My most basic belief is this: man does not stand somehow apart from nature – we *are* nature."

He sniffed and nodded shortly. "Nature, red in tooth and claw."

I nodded. "Red in tooth and claw, certainly. We are savage, like animals. We are brutal. But like animals, we are not *only* that that – and that was Caulderson's blindness." I paused for a moment, thinking of how to make him understand. At last, a remembrance struck me: a fragment of something I had read once that had surprised me, and stayed with me.

I dared to take his left hand, his empty hand, between my own, and recited what I could remember:

O'er all that moves,
O'er all that leaps, and runs, and shouts, and sings,
Or beats the gladsome air, o'er all that glides
Beneath the wave, yea, in the wave itself
In all things
I saw one life, and felt that it was joy.

He looked at me with desolate eyes, and I could not read his thoughts at all. Perhaps I was wrong to mention joy. My heart was too full, though, to – I kissed him, only once, on the mouth. I could not forbear. Whether he understood my meaning, I cannot say.

He smiled a little, though, and kissed me in return, but softly he said, as if to himself, "How strange to be so unrecognizable to oneself. How terrible, to live an unfamiliar story."

I shivered, suddenly chilled. He did not, then, understand me at all. "How freeing," I said, "how beautiful that we might write our own."

He sighed. "It is not so easy as that, Em."

"Nor is it impossible." I am not a patient man, but would learn patience for him.

He did not answer, but handed me the revolver. I have locked it in my strong box and will not return it.

Chapter Nine:
December 1851 – August 1852

22 December, 1851

TO: Vice Admiral Joseph Baring
British Navy
London Office

Baring,

And still, despite your inquiries, we have no word of the *Serapis*? I assume you would have written immediately had you received news.

I fear what this may mean. Even if the ship is still viable, the crew must already have exhausted their rations, and they are not equipped for extended Arctic service. How long can I be expected to wait, Joseph? He is, after all, my son. Should we not *act*?

Sir Francis Hall
Ashfield Manor
Caterham on the Hill, Surrey

* * * * *

TELEGRAPHIC MESSAGE: Vice Admiral Joseph Baring to Sir Francis Hall (23 December, 1851)

GET A HOLD OF YOURSELF STOP YOU LANDSMEN ARE ALWAYS SO QUICK TO WRITE US OFF STOP STAY THE COURSE STOP THERE IS AS YET NO CAUSE FOR PANIC STOP

* * * * *

Ship's Log
24 December 1851

The results of our hunting expeditions near the ship yield ever fewer kills, the plentiful game of the fall season giving way to winter barrenness. On the 22nd, a small party departed the ship on a hunting expedition of several days' duration: I leading, and bringing with me Taylor, Sainsbury, Kennedy, and Warde, the fittest of the crew. It is difficult to hunt in this darkness, but the moon is bright enough that we do not fear losing our way, at least. Two men pulled sledges, our hope being to load them with meat before our return in several days.

Our journey was a severe and tiring one. On the morning of our departure, it was 35° below zero, and alternated several degrees above and below that during the journey. Our route lay over the ice, some of which was heavy and packed, but some of it was of the previous year's formation, and very rough on the sledges.

The cold was intense: much worse than on our previous overland expedition. Our garments were always frozen after a march, stockings and boots adhering so firmly to each other, from the condensation of vapor, that we were often obliged to cut them off our feet, which might be said to be encased in ice. We kept in constant motion to prevent being frostbitten. The mitts were in the same condition, together with other portions of our dress; the only means for thawing them was by taking them into our blanket bags when we went to rest, and imparting to them the warmth of our own bodies. The consequence was that the product of the thaw, water, froze on our bags, which ultimately became hard and stiff from the accumulation of ice. Everything was either half-thawed, frozen, or covered with hoar-frost, not excepting eyelids, beard, and face, with frost-bites constantly occurring. We were frequently frost-bitten when asleep, or when in the act of dispatching our hasty meal, while sitting up in the tent, enveloped in our blankets.

Such are a few of the incidents of Arctic travelling, in the performance of which no service more thoroughly tests man's powers of endurance, both morally and physically. We stopped as little as possible – a few hours each night – but night being no different than day in quality of light or in temperature, it made little difference to our bone-deep exhaustion.

Our hunting party saw few successes: not enough, indeed, to justify the extra expenditure of rations which were required to sustain us on the journey. Worse, we suffered several serious injuries. Yesterday, while in pursuit of reindeer at a temperature of 36° below zero, Taylor's gun burst in his hands when in the act of firing, shattering the stock. His hands and forearms were grievously injured, and he was severely frostbitten in the aftermath of the injury. A similar circumstance occurred later the same day to Kennedy. With two injured men and a seeming inability to bring down large prey, I ordered the expedition back to the ship.

* * * * *

Surgeon's Log
24 December 1851

The ill-advised hunting party has returned. Our men held out well: all suffer from exhaustion and frostbite, and Taylor and Kennedy have superficial wounds to their hands and arms that will certainly prevent them from holding a rifle again for the foreseeable future, but all should recover reasonably well, given the constraints of our current circumstances.

Sickbay is full, and the list of complaints grows daily. Most will recover with proper diet and conditions, and a steady supply of anti-scorbutics. Without these things…

Milner, I fear, will not recover regardless. He suffers greatly – worse than the others – and his intellect has now been affected. He is in a state of complete imbecility, and a source of much trouble and anxiety; he was, on one occasion, found climbing to the upper decks with nothing but a thin blanket wrapped around his shoulders. Fortunately he was noticed and returned to me, but he must be watched constantly.

I fear to trouble the Captain with my reports, and yet the truth cannot be kept from him. Our situation grows more dire with every passing day.

❋ ❋ ❋ ❋ ❋

Naturalist's Log
24 December 1851

I write now with a graphite pencil, all the ink on board having frozen. We have not sufficient coal to keep the temperature steadily above freezing anywhere except the mess and the sickbay.

David and his idiotic hunting party have returned more dead than alive. The man nearly froze himself to death in order to provide a Christmas meal for his crew – and to what end? Bah. His instinct for self-destruction is staggering.

And yet what I can say to him? He is my captain, always, and I have no cogent argument to make. I, reduced to wordless sensation: helpless terror and furious want.

A year ago... A year ago, he embraced me for the first time. How changed am I! I cannot – I will not – live without –

✲ ✲ ✲ ✲ ✲

Ship's Log
25 December 1851

As difficult as our last Christmas seemed to us at the time, we now look back upon it with fondness and regret, for we were snug enough in our ship, and well fed. Now, all is silent and dark. Smith has no reserves with which to mark the holiday, and I have no Christmas meal to offer these good men, and nothing with which to fill their bellies. Only a triple ration of rum to warm them and the captain's ration of coal to add to the meager allowance that heats the mess.

The men are weakening. I have cancelled the daily hunt. They shall spend the day at rest.

✲ ✲ ✲ ✲ ✲

At the winter settlement far to the east of Anjikuni, Kingmiatook whispered to her daughter Osha:

In the darkest hours of the darkest days, when brother moon and sister sun are below the horizon, we must watch the dark sky, just there. At the rising of the bright star Akkuktujut, we will know that daylight is about to return and it is time for celebration.

On the first day the sun reappears, we all begin a new life. We must prepare for that now, do you see? We must be ready. Look, we have many good skins; these we must sew into kamleika. You will need a new atajuq soon, too. I will show you how to make it; we will do it together.

And here is a surprise! I saved a little agutak. Did you know we can mix it with snow, like this, and eat it up, sweet and fat? My mother made it for me once, when I was a girl. Here, try a little. Good girl. Eat it up, my good daughter.

✲ ✲ ✲ ✲ ✲

Captain's Log
11 January 1852

It is so dark, and so very cold. There is no daytime anymore, nor nighttime. Meals take but a moment. Nothing with which to mark the days. Hunting is difficult, with so many ill and our two best men injured. Sainsbury makes a mighty effort to fill Taylor's shoes, but game is so scarce that what he manages to bring in provides barely a morsel for each man. Increasingly, we pass the time abed, hoarding what strength and warmth and comfort still remains. I am loath to give orders to the contrary, and Carruthers concurs. With less effort expended, we can manage on less food.

✲ ✲ ✲ ✲ ✲

14 January 1852

TO: Miss H. Crawley
#3 West Hill Place
Brighton

Dear Miss Crawley,

God grant that this letter finds you in good spirits. I have been gratified to witness your slow return to health in the past weeks, and flatter myself that I may have played some small role in easing your way. No doubt Mrs. Maxwell's kind attendance has also had some small effect.

Permit me to say that I hold you in very high esteem. You have not, I know, had an easy life. Your father was always a hard man, and his final illness made him harder still. Your steadfast devotion, despite these unfavourable circumstances, your sweetness of demeanour and most womanly gentleness have made a great impression upon me.

Indeed, I have long harboured what I would characterize as a profound interest in your wellbeing, and since your father's death I have wished only to assist you in making your way in the world, in whatever capacity I can. I have watched you grow and mature, I have watched you keep a chaste and admirable character in most provoking circumstances, and – I have nurtured certain hopes within my breast.

Hannah, my dear. Permit me to help you, now. Permit me to lift you out of your terrible financial straits. Permit me to clasp you to my breast and protect you from harm. Permit me to marry you, Hannah, to take you as my wife: to honour, to cherish!

As a token of my very deep sincerity, I have taken the liberty of settling all of your father's debts. I have done so without ulterior motive, but only in the hopes of pleasing you. It is my dearest hope that you will, in return, find it in your heart to wish to please me, as well.

Take your time to consider the matter. You no longer require medical attention, and I will not return to Brighton until I receive an answer, so as not to influence or pressure your decision.

Yours in hope,

Dr. Barnabas Brown
#9 Harley Street
London W1

⚬ ⚬ ⚬ ⚬ ⚬

Naturalist's Log
15 January 1852

Some of my habits have fallen away due to the harshness of the conditions. I have not measured the thickness of the ice. Thus far in January, the temperature has fallen lower than has ever been experienced by any former Expedition – to 55° below zero, and in the interval of the usual period for taking the observations it fell to -63°, as the force of the wind was likewise greater. The mean temperature of the month is so far 43.87° below zero, lower than we had known it during any former winter, and, I believe, surpassing in degree anything recorded in former Polar voyages. I cannot properly remember the details of the previous record; my mind begins to muddle. 6 January was the coldest day that has ever been known in these latitudes – the mean temperature for twenty-four hours was 61°.6 below zero – from which some idea may perhaps be formed of the intensity of the cold.

The men cram into the mess for as long as they can countenance the close quarters; it is the only place we feel any semblance of warmth. It is difficult to bear the proximity of so many men, but when David raps on my cabin door, I permit him to convince me to accompany him thither for our daily hour of candlelight. He sits close to me, then, closer than propriety would allow – but at these temperatures, so does everyone else. The dim light seems very dazzling, after the dark. I can see his face, and he mine, and that is worth a very great deal. I shall stop writing here: I have better things to look on in the brief light. I long for him. He is here, beside me, and I long for him. A veil parts, sometimes, and –

* * * * *

15 January, 1852

TO: Abiah Higginbotham
37 Upper Hannover Street
Sheffield

Dearest Abiah,

Did I really wish for excitement in my last letter? I rescind my wish! I entirely rescind it. You shall never guess what has happened!

The frankly lecherous old doctor, Barnabas Brown, has attempted to *purchase* our Hannah – right out from under her absent fiancé! Can you imagine such impertinence? It quite takes my breath away – but then, I should know better than to underestimate such men. What do you think he has done? He has bought up her debts, or I should say, her father's debts. Thousands, Abiah! Thousands of pounds! I have seen the accounts myself. Hannah is quite frantic; I had to restrain her from flying to him at once, not knowing what she might do. Lord! For all I know, she would have married the man on the spot in gratitude. She is entirely confounded, as am I – although I with rather more rage than she professes.

Lord! I do not have the first idea of what to say to her. I greatly fear that for her, the path to destruction and salvation is the same.

The – the *man*, I suppose, for Hannah has forbidden me from calling him names – the man has said he will not darken our doorstep until Hannah makes her decision. Well for him. I fear what I would do, if I saw his face.

Counsel me, friend. My mind is all chaos.

Addie Maxwell
#3 West Hill Place
Brighton

* * * * *

Captain's Log
19 January 1852

The men are hungry, cold, sick, and wretched. We have light in the mess, now, for one hour each day, which is how I write this Log. The exception is sickbay, where Carruthers has free rein to use candles as required. My personal ration of candles and coal has gone to sickbay. We cannot exercise above deck in this cold; we have no energy to spare even for hunting. We lie abed and preserve what strength we have. We wait for the sun.

* * * * *

Surgeon's Log
21 January 1852

Now, we can only wait. The spring will come, or we will die – as to which will happen first, it is anyone's guess. George Milner has finally succumbed to scurvy. He hung on much longer than I expected, but now his suffering is at an end. The captain has designated a corner of the orlop deck the deadroom; it is frigid in those depths, and we cannot bury him either at land or at sea until the thaw.

I keep the illest men in sickbay, where they will at least be warm: Billy Newton is here, and Evans. Too, Griggs and Wynniatt – all with rapidly advancing scurvy. Quarters are very tight. Many others are failing, as well, and all aboard ship are now on the sick list in some capacity. I'd wager Hall's condition is worse than he lets on, but I will not pry, for I have no means to cure or even aid him. Sainsbury is surely the strongest of all of us; he must have the constitution of an ox. He continues to hunt, though not every day, and without much success. Young Harry Sykes worries me; a boy of his years should not be subject to such limited rations. I slip him my own when I can.

* * * * *

[Paper fragment crumpled]

February 1852

TO: Dr. Brown
Harley Street

Dear Sir,

Thank you for your

My Dear Sir,

I cannot tell you with what a thankful heart I recei

* * * * *

Surgeon's Log
2 February 1852

Henry Stone was found dead in his bunk this morning. I had not been monitoring him, as he was not apparently any sicker than the rest, he was not even in sickbay, but in the main mess with the others. What he died of – I cannot say with certainty. He died of this place. We are all dying of it. I have lost three teeth since yesterday.

We've moved Stone to the dead room below decks. I will endeavor to check the condition of each man aboard, morning and night, though there is little I can do for them.

* * * * *

Captain's Log
8 February 1852

If only there were something I could do! And yet I am tired – so tired. So cold. My thinking grows muddled sometimes; as if I am in a dark fog. And there is nothing at all to do but to lie in the dark and pray for sleep. Even at mess, the men speak little. Embleton and I speak little. I know that he is not well.

Last winter was a time of shared feeling and mutual fellowship amongst the men. This winter, less is shared and more is hoarded. I do not know if I wish for life or death. I wish life for my men. I must wish life for them.

I wrestle with Caulderson in the dark, for hours, his hands around my throat, until sleep takes me, or Smith rings the bell for rations. He has taken to locking the store room and wearing the key around his neck.

✲ ✲ ✲ ✲ ✲

Naturalist's Log
13? 18? February? 1852

I do not

It is dark. I write by feel. It is only instinct to record,
I believe, but he is here with me now,

and I will not leave my bunk while he is in it. Not for some paltry rations, not for light. We have light. We have light here, between us, and warmth. I have him, there is nothing else I

He came to me – when? An hour ago? A day? I did not know if I dreamed.

"Help me," he whispered. "You took away my revolver – you consigned me to this. Help me, now." I could not tell if he was angry, but as he spoke, he raised the blanket on the bed and crawled in beside me, throwing his own over top of us as well. He grasped my arms and shook me. He was

> real. He hurt my arm. His words were anguished, but he was strong in his rage. "Help me to feel it, to bear it. I don't know how to –"

We were wrestling. Or were we loving? The ring he wore cut at my flesh. Was he crying? I could not – Was I?

"Always, David. Always." I touched his face because I could not see him in the dark, and he touched mine. In the touching, I saw. I saw him. We slept, and woke, and slept again, until the two merged together in some eternal and unchanging stasis. Sometimes he

spoke, perhaps a word or a sentence, sometimes struggling to speak the needful thing, and sometimes not speaking it. ό, τι δεν μπορούμε να πούμε θα είναι έκλαψε, it is true, it is true, I hear, I believe I understand.

All was touching. All. The very air was our touching. And we were one. I felt the wound in his heart – how can I express this? I felt it as if it pierced my own, as if I could no longer tell, in the dark, which wound was his and which was mine; my body, my very mind, grew permeable, and when he pressed himself to me, the pain was so great that I was

> breathless, for a time, and dizzy with it, but his breath beside me drew me back to myself, and he breathed for me then, and I for him, and the wound – the pain was again bearable – and his breathing eased, and I touched

his face and felt fingers on my own, and that gossamer barrier between us, that barrier that separates the essence of all living things, it was gone, gone, gone.

Is there a word for this? A word to make it real? *Siamo il ghiaccio*, dissolving and resolidifying, *un cicolo terrible*, sublime. He my solvent and I his. Solvation, that is the word. No: *salvazione. Il liquido diviene cristallo*, volume becomes mass, mass becomes an anchor. *Mi ancoro in lui e lui* in me.

How can I be his anchor when my body is floating away?

We are so tired. We sleep too much. We are warm together.

His face. His face. I see it with my fingers. I feel it on my tongue.

David, I was wrong about writing our own story. We are not writing at all, but rather learning to read it in the darkness.

Wenn es so sein soll dass wir hier sterben, so werden wir zumindest dies gehabt haben.

I will have loved. I must master myself. I feel drugged. It is so hard to believe oneself real in this darkness. I must not –

We are dying.

We are dying, ό, τι δεν μπορούμε να πούμε θα είναι έκλαψε

* * * * *

Captain's Log
February 1852

I take up my pen – my pencil – once more, and it feels strange between my fingers. I am clumsy as a child. How long were we holed up in Embleton's cabin? Two days? Three? More? God. I recall Smith brought us rations once – or was it twice? How long?

It was but a moment, a moment separate from the world, for us alone. What is that poem? I cannot think at all … *This bed thy center is, these walls, thy sphere.*

This bed thy center is. I never wished to leave. It was so – We were warm. I hurt when I came to him; hurt so that I thought I would die of it. And he – he drew the poison from me. He loves me. I think the pain began to abate when I saw that – ha! I saw that, finally, when I was blind in the darkness. He loves me. He loves me! He whispered this to me, again and again until I believed with my – with the stuff of my body. Mind be damned – I believe him with my flesh. We merged together, in that bed. We were one, and for that moment, nothing hurt.

It was Embleton who woke us from this beautiful fog. It was he – it is ever he – who saves us. Perhaps we were dying. He believes we were. I did not know that I slept, but I woke to him shaking me, shaking me hard, forcing me to rise, wrapping my blanket around my shoulders and leading me to the mess.

How we trembled, weak and cold. We newborns.

In the mess, I ordered Smith, lying by the stove, to light the candle. It quite blinded me, and I shrank away from the light. As my vision cleared, I saw the sorry state of us. The men lie in rows, motionless and groggy. Smith rose and went slowly to the store room, returning with a hard biscuit and a little cocoa for each. Most had to moisten their biscuit to be able to bite it. They are losing teeth now. There was silence, except for someone's wracking cough – Rob Tiffeny, I think.

Embleton, though! He is like a man possessed. He paces furiously, skipping nimbly over outstretched legs and muttering to himself as he goes. It makes me dizzy to look at him, and so I have taken out my little log book and my pencil, and here I sit.

He cannot think his way out of this.

* * * * *

Naturalist's Log
February 1852

I have it. I have it!

It is the foxes – we must be foxes, we must

I must go; there is no time to lose. If only I can…

* * * * *

17 February 1852

Dearest Addie,

When I open my mouth to speak to you, words desert me and my courage fails. Perhaps my pen will allow me to properly express my thoughts. If you love me, read this letter. Please read it, and with kindness. Your silence these past weeks, while I have wrestled with this terrible decision that lies before me, has been – intolerable. It has been more intolerable than your anger was, to begin with; indeed, I almost prefer you angry to cold, for at least then I know your mind.

God help me, I am so alone. I almost miss my father.

Addie, you must see that I have no choice in the matter at hand. Lew is gone. He took – he took the best and truest part of me, and vanished, and I am ruined. I know you still pray for your husband's return, but for my part, I have abandoned that hope. I cannot gamble my life on the slim chance of their return. I must do the best I can for myself. I must be pragmatic, and think of my future.

I am *vastly* indebted to Dr. Brown. He has placed me irrevocably in his power – you deny this, but it is plainly true. And is it so very terrible, at that? I do not love the man, of course, but I do not believe that he would ever strike me, or force me, or harm me in any way. I have endured much worse in my lifetime. I cannot live off of your kindness forever. Two women together – it is not the way of things. Surely you see that? Your husband will come home one day, Addie, or he will not, and you will marry again, and then what shall become of me? I need a home of my own. I need a *real* home, and he is offering it to me.

Addie, you have seen how wretched I have been. Can you not now wish me happiness?

You are the best – nay. In truth, you are the *only* true friend I have had in my life. Please try to understand me, Addie. Please persist. Ah, why is this grief so profound? I thought I should be happy.

Your friend always,

Hannah

✲ ✲ ✲ ✲ ✲

18 February 1852

My Hannah,

Oh, I shall love you to pieces until the end of our days, you stupid, stupid girl, *only do not do this.* Do not throw yourself away on such a man, for such a reason. Your value is – it is more than he can know. Whether or not the *Serapis* returns is immaterial: we cannot know the future. Are we not happy now, as we are? Can we not go on in this way? Why must things change? Why is our home not *real* to you? Can you imagine that I would ever cast you out? If David and Lew return home, so be it. If not, again, so be it. We shall endure.

Listen: you must permit yourself to imagine different ways for the story of your life to unfold. It is difficult, my dear. I know it is. The path is obscure and full of terror. *You are strong enough to bear it,* and when you fail, or when I fail, we shall bear it together.

If you wish it, we shall bear it together.

Addie

✲ ✲ ✲ ✲ ✲

Ship's Log
27 February 1852

Once again is our mission indebted to naturalist Hall's ingenuity. We have passed a terrible month – these past two weeks, most especially. We are cold and we sicken and starve. He has invented a scheme for supplementing the nutritional intake of the crew. It has made a sudden and marked improvement in the condition of the men, as has the painfully gradual reappearance of light in the sky. The effect on morale of just a few minutes of light on the horizon cannot be overstated. Despite the excessive cold, I order the men who are well enough up to the main deck to see it every day; to bask and take note of its ever-lengthening promise.

Hall's discovery is this: that in observing and then emulating the habits of the Arctic fox, we may discover large invisible colonies of mice and lemmings living under the snow cover, and trap these in sufficient numbers to feed ourselves. His early experiments have proven most successful, and resulted in a nutrient-rich slurry that was entirely disgusting, but nevertheless was devoured by the crew. With Smith's assistance he has found a slightly more palatable formulation.

Hall assures me that a bowlful of this stew, issued twice per day, will keep men alive through a winter. It is far more sustaining – and results in much better health – than the severely reduced rations upon which we had been subsisting.

He has drafted Sainsbury, May, and Hulott, the healthiest remaining men, into service, constructing and setting ingenious traps which he takes out onto the ice, morning and evening, to deposit under the snow cover in specific placement formations understood only by him. He claims to have learned the technique from observing the foxes during our protracted overland expedition. However he has done it, the man has all but assured our survival through this terrible winter. I can see the men grow stronger again before my eyes.

✲ ✲ ✲ ✲ ✲

Book of Recipes for Ship Cooking
Her Majesty Queen Victoria's Royal Navy
Ex Libris Lowery Smith, 1832

Handwritten inside the back cover:

Mouse Stew (February 1852)

Skin and eviscerate a large number of mice, rats, and lemmings – as many as you are able to obtain.

Separate the bones from the meat of the animals, and place the bones, along with whatever savoury herbs you have to hand, into a cauldron of good, fresh water with a little salt. Boil to draw the goodness from the bones and obtain a savoury stock.

Once the bones are boiled clean and stripped of all marrow, strain them out and then add the meat to the stock along with the daily vegetable ration and a small rasher of salt pork for flavor. An onion would be most beneficial but is presently out of our reach. Cook to reduce the stew to a favourable thickness.

If you can spare a spoonful or two of oats per man, this will fortify the stew most agreeably.

The men should prefer the savoury stew baked in a pie if such luxury is within your means.

The caldron should never be allowed to run dry, but should be refreshed with daily additions of meat &c. In this way its flavour improves.

The flavour of the mice is no different from rabbit, while lemmings are reminiscent of partridges.

* * * * *

Surgeon's Log
28 February 1852

Perhaps I should not say so, for fear of angering the capricious gods, but I believe the worst of the danger has now passed. Hall's innovative foodstuff appears to be as nutritious as it is disgusting – which is to say, very – and the pervasive feeling of imminent doom under which we have passed much of this winter seems to be lightening with the sky itself. I can remove no men from the sick list, for the scurvy is still advancing and that will not change until we can harvest fresh plants in the true spring, but hunger subsides, and that makes a great difference to what human bodies can withstand.

* * * * *

Many seasons later, when Osha was old enough to understand, Kingmiatook told her the story.

That winter, the winter after the terrible coming of the qallunaat, after all the deaths, it was very cold, very hard. We had not seen one like it in many years, and we all suffered from it. Even after we rejoined father's camp, it was not easy.

We prepared for many days, many nights, in the cold and dark. When we first saw the small light of the sun in the sky – how great was our relief. The children ran singing to blow out the flames of every qulliq, to remove the old wicks and relight the lamps with a new one. Then the men made their nunajisartung, dancing and singing, following the course of the sun. We women had our gifts prepared: meat, ivory, pieces of good sealskin. No one was forgotten.

Then we had the contest of the seasons; the children of winter, the axigirn, took up one side of a rope of sealskin, and the children of the summer, the aggirn, took up the other. They pulled and pulled against each other, and we who watched held our breath – for if the axigirn prevail, summer has won the game and the coming year will be an easy one. It was not clear, for long minutes, who would win – but the summer took it at last, and loud were our cheers then.

At last, tall and lumbering, with a sealskin mask and long spears, the qailertetang came over the ice. Children screamed – no, not you, my brave girl – and women fell back before him. Men began to run, pursued by the qailertetang, to the huts of their women, where they were for the following day nulianitititjung. Having performed this duty, the qailertetang invoked the good north wind, which brings fair weather, and danced to warn off the unfavourable south wind.

As soon as the incantation was over, all the men remaining in the circle attacked the qailertetang with great noise, acting as if they had weapons in their hands and would kill the spirit. One seemed to probe him with a spear, another to stab him with a knife, one to cut off his arms and legs, another to beat him unmercifully on the head. The robes he wore were ripped open and soon lay strewn beside his body on the snow. Then we each took up our drinking cups and passed them to the qailertetang, awakening him to new life.

We feasted, then, on igunaq, and prayed together that the next year would be better for us.

✲ ✲ ✲ ✲ ✲

Naturalist's Log
16 March 1852

I am kept very occupied with the trapping and processing of small Arctic mammals, and have not had the leisure to keep up with this log. Most of my measurements have fallen away, although I can report at least that the cold continued very severe in the month of February, the mean of which being 48.5° below zero. March, thus far, is not appreciably warmer. The winter has been throughout unparalleled in its rigour and severity. At a future date, I shall record the details of my traps: physical dimensions; efficacy with various species; &c., &c. But at present, I am focused entirely upon the unexpected task of feeding a ship-full of men.

David sleeps with me now. Every night. I would not – we cannot be separate. We have lost all fear of disapprobation. It is warm. It is right. There is no room left in us for fear.

⁂

Ship's Log
28 March 1852

Temperatures warm with almost agonizing slowness, but aboard ship our conditions have improved to such an extent that I have been able to order day expeditions of two to four men charged with gathering any firewood or brush they might find on the shore and hauling it back, as well as hunting any game they come across. To enable us to withstand the fatigue of the short expeditions, we are obliged to eat the greater portion of our ration of stew. In the past several weeks, our united efforts have enabled us to procure a brace of hare and a single reindeer, which yielded 94 lbs. of meat for general use. It does perhaps speak to our desperation for good meat that the blood of the deer that was killed was eagerly drunk by the hunter as it flowed fresh and warm from the wound, for the vivifying and sustaining influence it exercised; but as it froze on the face as it flowed, he presented a frightful spectacle on coming on board.

⁂

29 March 1852

TO: Dr. Barnabas Brown
#9 Harley Street
London W1

Dear, good Dr. Brown,

I write to thank you for your endless kindness to me, for your unearned regard, and – most especially, sir – for your patience, which I have sorely tried in the past weeks.

I am deeply honoured by and grateful for your attentions, sir. And equally, I am surprised almost to the point of incredulity. I had not entertained the slightest thought of ever earning your regard, and to have done so all unaware fills me with a sense of paralyzing astonishment. That you – good, kind, wise sir – should think of me at all!

And then, there is the matter of your too-great generosity! – for which I cannot ever thank you enough, and for which I shall never be able to repay you. You are too good, dear sir, and far too kind.

Please understand that I have undergone a rapid and extremely trying change in my personal circumstances once in the past year, and it nearly shattered my health entirely. Indeed, I recovered only thanks to your solicitous care. To contemplate another great change of life – pleasant though it may be – is something that requires time and thought and care. I cannot bear to move swiftly.

I shall not try your patience much longer, sir. I shall answer you as soon as I can do so in good health and good cheer.

Most sincerely,

Hannah Crawley
#3 West Hill Place
Brighton

* * * * *

Captain's Log
17 April 1852

I must prepare the men to make a final push; one last effort to withdraw and return home. My concern now is to feed them as much as possible, to shore up their health by whatever means I possibly can, and to prepare the ship for sailing. We must be in excellent shape when the melt finally comes. We all know that this is our final chance. We will not survive another winter.

Embleton has worked himself to the bone these last six weeks. I fear for his health. He is out in the snow with his traps at all hours of the day and night. This though the game animals have begun to return from lands to the south and we find ever more success at the chase. He does not eat even a half of his own rations, and at night I can easily feel his bones through his skin.

I shall ask Carruthers to have a word with him. I know Embleton respects him as a man of science.

⁂ ⁂ ⁂ ⁂ ⁂

Ship's Log
2 May 1852

Our mission for the month of May is to ballast and water the ship preparatory to our expected liberation. The men who have not been completely prostrated by the scurvy are strong enough for it, I believe, after several months of Hall's excellently efficacious and nourishing stew. Taylor has almost completely recovered from his hunting misadventure, and is stuck in with the rest of them. He has the strength of a bear, but they are all exceptionally motivated to work quickly and to work well.

⁂ ⁂ ⁂ ⁂ ⁂

Surgeon's Log
23 May 1852

The captain is working the men harder than I would prefer, but what can I say? For if we are not absolutely prepared to sail at the first possible thaw – well. We are all dead men, anyway.

Their eyes are now much exposed to the combined influence of snow and sunshine, as the ballast is all collected on the still snow-covered land, and firmly frozen in the soil, whence it is dragged on sledges through soft thawing snow to the ship – a work of no light nature. The consequence is that opthalmia (snow blindness) has become very general amongst them. Upwards of one third of the able-bodied crew are affected; although I have suggested the precaution of wearing crape veils or glasses, the usual imprudence of the sailor has prevailed.

A second party of men is at work in taking in our supply of water, which was found of good quality in a small lake about a mile distant inland. This continued laborious work – on men who have previously been making great exertions on an inadequate diet – has produced the effects that might have been anticipated. They revert to that altered and haggard aspect which they wore through the worst of the winter, and they complain of a feeling of general languor, weakness, and debility. Fortunately, the warmer weather has seen the return of large game, and we have had better luck with hunting than we have seen in many months. Fresh meat is now issued in larger quantity and more frequently. This has the added benefit of permitting Hall to cease his labours on the ice with his traps and his mice. The man worked tirelessly, and truly, his exertions saved all our lives this dreadful winter. But he is exhausted. He must stop. I shall have the captain order it if I must.

✲ ✲ ✲ ✲ ✲

Ship's Log
4 June 1852

The internal work of the ship has commenced. The thickness of the ice on the first of June was found to be eight inches more than last year. We do not know with any certainty when the ship will be released, but by God, we shall be ready.

✲ ✲ ✲ ✲ ✲

Naturalist's Log
9 June 1852

"Rest," they say. Ha! Rest? As if a man could rest in the midst of this! It is a waste to sleep an hour – a minute! A specimen of the North American Crane was shot on the third – it was a noble looking bird, was two feet high, had an expanse of wing of four feet, and weighed eight lbs. I have not yet completed my anatomical drawings and measurements. The Golden Plover (*Charadrius Pluviahs*), the Phalerope (*Phalaropus Platyrynchos*), the Purple Sandpiper (*Tringa Maritimal*), and the Sanderling (*Calidris Arenaria*) have been sighted, and I do not yet have specimens. Another wolf adventure had likewise occurred with the boatswain, who, when in pursuit of a deer, saw it suddenly stop on the top of a hill about 300 yards distant; at the same moment several wolves (ten in number) made their appearance in quick succession, none of which had been previously seen. They formed a circle around the affrighted deer, and in a crouching position gradually closed on him. Suddenly, as if by some preconcerted signal, they all sprang on the animal, and immediately brought it to the ground. Kennedy reports that he watched the scene for a time – would that I had been there! – then fired two shots at the wolves and advanced towards them, when they decamped. About fifteen minutes had elapsed from the time he first saw the wolves, and there was nothing of the deer remaining but the skin, with the spine, antlers, part of the head, and bones of a hind leg, the rest having been devoured. The bones he brought on board for me. They were cleanly picked, with small shreds of flesh adhering (which I have preserved, presently finding skin and the process of tanning quite extraordinarily fascinating), and provided poor consolation for my having missed so fascinating a scene. Speaking of tanning, I am perfecting my technique on mouse skins, thinking to create a patchwork flag for our ship as we are all indebted to them for our very lives. Ha! We shall fly the mouse flag yet. Two snow geese were also shot by one of our men. Oh! The hunting is excellent now, and the men well pleased to share their findings with me. And then there is David! There is so much I do not know about him; why, I have sought to catalogue the precise colour variations in his hair since we met, and I am not close to making a final determination. There is so very much to do before –

✲ ✲ ✲ ✲ ✲

Ship's Log
16 June 1852

This morning, the first appearance of water on the ice: a pool a few inches deep, and this afternoon the first rain of the season fell. If this year follows the pattern of the last, the thaw shall progress more rapidly now. Ashore, water has begun to run through the little ravines, and the river is almost entirely free of ice. The men are near wild with relief.

✲ ✲ ✲ ✲ ✲

Captain's Log
18 June 1852

All is well with the ship, at last, and yet – all is not well with Embleton. He has run himself ragged, and will not stop to eat or rest or even speak to me. It is as if he were running from the Devil himself. Carruthers has had stern words with him, I know, and yet to no effect. He grows so thin and pale, and jerks about, and takes every excuse to spend time with his damned tanning… He will not speak to me about anything of any importance. When I mention home, or London, or anything of the sort, he shuts up like a clam! I should perhaps be concerned that his regard for me has changed, but the way he clings to me at night – no. I cannot believe it. It is something else.

Once, early on in our acquaintance, Embleton told me about this strange turn in his nature: he has periods in which he works endlessly, tirelessly, madly – his mind prods him ever on and he cannot stop himself.

And then – when the job is done – he collapses, prostrate. I have not witnessed such a period before, but I believe this is what is happening to him now. It is difficult for me to observe it, and yet what can I do? Fighting against him is as impossible as fighting the Arctic ice. This drive is implacable, and it will release him when it wills, and not a moment sooner.

✲ ✲ ✲ ✲ ✲

Naturalist's Log
19 June 1852

The captain has permitted a final expedition over the ice to shore. This morning, I proceeded with an attendant (Clem Basting – a surprisingly acceptable self-taught geologist) to the hills on the opposite side of the bay, to remove some specimens and complete my geological examination of the land, insomuch as any examination can ever be called "complete." In my course I visited two small islands in the center of the Bay; they possessed no interest, except in affording evidence of their having been at one period visited by the Esquimeaux in their migration along the coast. A few large masses of sandstone and clay-slate were collected on their summits, and a sort of embankment was thrown up around them, from the pressure of the ice.

There is much more I could record of the mineral composition of the soil, &c., but this shall have to await full analysis in my home laboratory. Home! Strange thought.

The excursion was a difficult one. From the progress of thaw, our course lay through soft snow and water, which so benumbed the feet and legs, that we were frequently obliged to stop, remove our boots and stockings, and by friction restore suspended animation. We regained the ship with considerable relief after ten hours of constant exertion.

David was in our – was in my cabin when I returned. He pressed supper upon me most tiresomely, and demanded I lay with him and rest.

It is impossible. There is so much yet to do. I cannot think of what may come.

✲ ✲ ✲ ✲ ✲

24 June 1852

TO: Doctor Barnabas Brown
#9 Harley Street
London W1

My dear sir,

I must begin this letter by acknowledging the kindness you have shown to me throughout my life, but most especially in this very difficult past year. I have no words to express how much your goodness has transformed my life for the better. I am fully sensible of the risk you have taken in forming this attachment to a poor, broken girl, but please believe that I shall strive to spend the remainder of my life ensuring that you never regret your choice.

And because I do not wish you to ever regret me, sir, I must tell you that there is a small matter upon which I cannot compromise. I have recently become involved with a Women's Committee. I believe you know which one I mean; it is the same to which Mrs. Maxwell belongs. I know you believe such work to be unduly taxing and improper, but sir, upon this point I shall not be swayed: my committee work, consisting only of monthly meetings and some light correspondence, will continue.

If you are amenable to this small foible of mine sir, then I am ready to give you an answer, and await only your coming. Mrs. Maxwell is away; I am at your disposal.

Most sincerely,

Hannah Crawley
#3 West Hill Place
Brighton

⁂ ⁂ ⁂ ⁂ ⁂

Ship's Log
2 July 1852

All last night and into the morning, the wind blew in strongly from the south-east, and soon afterwards a lane of water opened about 80 yards from the ship, extending due east and west, with the ice in the offing drifting to the westward, while that in our vicinity was quite stationary. We waited breathlessly, watching. Towards noon, as the wind became south-west, it resumed its easterly drift, and a short distance from the ship we saw loose sailing ice, which, could we then have reached, our progress to the eastward might have been considerable – the drift being estimated at upwards of a mile an hour. How agonizing was it to stand on deck, stationary, and see liberation so near at hand, and so out of reach! Such was the case for the rest of the long day. It must be soon.

⁂ ⁂ ⁂ ⁂ ⁂

Captain's Log
2 July 1852

Three hours of ordering – of begging! And the stubborn bastard won't – He is the only one with the experience and scientific knowledge needed to properly set a charge. If he will not, no one can. He makes no sense. No sense at all! It's as if he does not wish to escape from this dreadful place, does not wish to go home! He refuses to discuss strategy, but sits on deck senselessly scraping at mouse skins. Bah! I know that the man is not heartless. He has nearly worked himself to death these last few months for the sake of his shipmates. He is not – he is not being rational. That is the issue. It is most out of character. I cannot think what to make of it.

* * * * *

Daily Telegraph
Page 12
2 July 1852

We publish the Banns of Marriage between Dr. Barnabas Brown of Harley Street and Miss Hannah Crawley, late of Brighton. This is the first time of asking. If any know cause or just impediment why these two persons should not be joined together in Holy Matrimony, ye are to declare it.

* * * * *

Naturalist's Log
3 July 1852

He always expects me to be better than I am. How can he not see? I have him here. I have him – he is mine, while we are here. In London? What would he want with a man such as I?

* * * * *

Ship's Log
3 July 1852

We experienced no change to our situation over the course of the night, and at an early hour in the morning it was deemed judicious to attempt a more active solution. A small cask of powder was placed beneath the outer barrier at a location most carefully measured out by Hall, which its explosion fractured; but this did not release us. The necessity of adopting all possible means to liberate the ship became then evident, as it was tantalizing to view, only 30 yards distant, such a fine space of open water that would have secured an easterly advance. Hall placed a heavy charge of 250 pounds in a rum cask, and sank it under the ice, which was about 16 feet thick, with five fathoms of fuse attached. The report was tremendous, and the shock was felt throughout the ship – then only about 25 yards distant from the blast. Its effect on the ice was admirable, smashing it in every direction, and casting numerous fragments on board. The grounded ice to which we were secured, varying in thickness from 35 to 67 feet, was rent in several places. This was the largest charge that has ever been used in ice navigation.

The greater part of the obstructing floe was broken up, or fissured in such a manner as to be easily set adrift; which the entire available ship's company, armed with handpicks or some equally efficient implements, shortly effected. Several smaller charges of powder were successfully exploded nearer the ship; still she remained motionless. We then made sail, and hove all aback with a view of loosening her attachments. Anchors were laid out and hove on at the capstan, and we attempted the usual expedients of sallying &c. After some time, our efforts were crowned with success, the ship became released, and buoyant, once more ready to move under her canvas.

The men were ordered an extra allowance of meat and spirits. All were overjoyed with our success of the day.

* * * * *

Captain's Log
3 July 1852

As the ship broke free from the ice at last – at last! – many men broke down in tears of relief. Hall did, and turned from me that I not see it. As if there is any part of him that I do not – that I do not love.

He wept, and I felt such unutterable tenderness that I struggled to maintain my own composure.

I love him. I am brave enough to feel it now, and even to say it. I nudged his arm with my own, and when he turned to me, his face wet, I did.

His eyes when I said the words – my God! My God, how I love him. He did not know. How could he not have known? After – after all? He looked at me quite as though I had struck him, cut him to the quick. Then he took a single, shuddering breath, and clasped me tightly to his breast. His body shook; he was laughing – laughing madly.

The men whooped and cheered and celebrated around us at the liberation of the ship; our embrace was remarked upon by none.

And then he was swaying, knees buckling, and he would have fallen to the ground had I not had a firm hold of him. I lowered him down as gently as I could, loosening his collar and calling his name.

His eyes fluttered open. "David," he breathed; beautiful, my name on his lips.

"Yes, love?" I whispered.

He smiled. "I am so tired. So tired."

This, then, was the crash after his months of tireless work. "I would imagine so. You've barely slept or eaten for months, love!" I could not stop saying it, once I started. "Come along, let's get you to bed."

He is safe now, tucked up in my bed – for I would have him nowhere else – and tended by Carruthers, who wakes him periodically to take some soup and watered brandy. The good doctor assures me he shall recover fully, now that he has allowed himself to rest.

This is the most terrifying thing I have faced these whole two years at sea: I need Embleton as I need air in my lungs. And yet, the terror is not unbearable. He will never willingly leave me; he cannot, any more than a heart can leave the body it animates. There is no life for either, apart.

✿ ✿ ✿ ✿ ✿

Ship's Log
5 July 1852

Accustomed as we were to the ice, to its caprices, and to its sudden and unexpected alterations, it was a change like that of magic to find that solid mass of ocean suddenly converted into water! Navigable, and navigable to us, who had almost forgotten what it was to float at freedom on the seas. It is at times scarcely to be believed, that our ship once more rises on the waves beneath us, and that when the winds blow, it obeys our will and our hands.

I had some initial concern that our present complement of less than 20 men on active duty would find it difficult to man and sail the ship effectively – but happily, such is not the case. I have had to lengthen the watches, but no man has complained. We are all too pleased to be moving once more.

⁂⁂⁂⁂⁂

Ship's Log
18 July 1852

We make remarkably swift progress eastward. Instead of retracing our route, we shall attempt the more southerly passage, keeping within sight of the mainland even when a more direct, and more northerly route would seem to be swifter – a most satisfactory choice, as it happens. In concert with Mr. Taylor, I estimate our making the east coast of the continent by mid-August; our passage across the Atlantic to last another 25 or 30 days. None of us wish to prolong our voyage with a provisioning detour to Halifax if we can possibly avoid it. Certainly, however, we stop at regular intervals along the shore to harvest large quantities of edible antiscorbutic plants, and to hunt. Already, Carruthers reports marked improvement in the most affected men.

* * * * *

26 July 1852

TO: Abiah Higginbotham
37 Upper Hannover Street
Sheffield

Abiah,

Today I saw my dear friend wed. Nothing I have said to her made any difference. She has chosen to allow herself to be purchased like a whore, and I cannot bear it, Abiah. I cannot bear it.

The most galling fact is that she has acted entirely reasonably – even I can see that. She has done *well* for herself, even. And yet – such piercing grief, that it must be so! That I must smile and kiss her and congratulate her *owner* when he takes my hand. You cannot imagine the terrible thoughts I had in that church; the dreadful things I imagined.

I am going abroad. I feel nothing but antipathy for my home, and nothing ties me to it. My husband is gone. My Hannah is sold. My country cares less for my sex than it cares for the welfare of animals. And I am dying from it. I must find a way to live with this anger that eats at me, growing stronger while I sicken. Only the thought of missing you dreadfully, as I know I shall, gives me pause. If I go, Abiah, will you promise to visit me?

I have taken a room in Paris, in Pigalle. You'll enjoy it there, my dear. Perhaps I will move often. Perhaps I will use a different name. Perhaps I will be a different person.

I wish now to put the life I have known behind me, and yet when I am on the ship I know I shall think of my David, sailing off somewhere on the same sea – for the seas are all connected, are they not? I know that you did not approve of or understand our arrangement, but it has truly been one of the great anchors of my life, and I miss him.

Write to me, won't you? Poste Restante Centrale, Paris. I shall look out for your letters. In truth, I shall rely upon them, for they will be my only anchor, now.

Addie

PS.: if my husband returns, as I feel certain he will, tell him – send him my love.

* * * * *

Ship's Log
7 August 1852

Excellent luck: this morning hailed a whaling vessel; the first we've seen two full years. It was well laden for the season, and the captain allowed us to purchase supplies: a small amount of salt horse, two barrels of molasses, three pounds of tea, eight pounds of sugar, and seven large sacks of weevily flour. There was even a small cask of lime, much to Carruthers' delight. The price named was exorbitant, but not a man raised protest. We shall subsist on this, along with fish, for the duration of the crossing and be well satisfied.

* * * * *

15 August 1852

TO: Mrs. Brown
#9 Harley Street
London W1

Dear Hannah,

I write to wish you well in your new life, and in the sincere hope that your union will be blessed with happiness, prosperity, and comfort. Please, my dear, forget that ugly scene; forget the words I said, and forgive me for my harshness. I am not angry with you – only with the world.

I love you, and I only ever wish you well.

I do not expect to see much of you in the coming years, as I am moving to the Continent for the foreseeable future. You have made a great change, and I must do the same. I must shape my life into something livable. At any rate, I must try.

Yours,
Addie Maxwell

* * * * *

Ship's Log
17 August 1852

We make steady progress; indeed, for all the difficulty we encountered on our way west, we now find only smooth waters, good winds, and clear channels in the opposite direction.

Today we took our last look at the shoreline of lower Canada, many men with curses on their lips. When the land was quite out of sight, we stopped to bury our dead comrades at sea – the men would not have them rest in that accursed land. It was a solemn ceremony, but our minds are lighter now that it is done. Home is within reach.

* * * * *

Kingmiatook told Osha how the story ends, for Osha to tell her own daughters one day, and their daughters after that:

Your father, our good Tukkuttok, wished to return to the terrible place: the place on the west side of Anjikuni where we used to go to hunt the spring deer at Kivalliq as they came down through Kazan River. I would not go with him. I would not allow him to take you. He went alone to that place, and this is what he told me.

He said that the iglu where Eqilaglu died, where Qannik and her children died, is caved in and snowed over and gone. He said many prayers at that place, and sang many songs to their spirits.

But also at that place, there was a strange inukshuk standing that he hadn't seen before. It was made very curiously; it spoke nothing that made sense. It was not of our people. He thought this inukshuk was cursed by the spirit who had left it there, who had caused the mad things to attack us. He thought that if he didn't pull it down, he'd catch sick and die, or if not he himself, we would die, Osha, you and I. So he took each stone and scattered it to the winds. He worked all day, until everything was gone – until it was torn right down to the ground, so no one will ever find a trace of it. Then he came home to us.

Chapter Ten: September – December 1852

Ship's Log
13 September 1852

We have been blessed with an easy crossing – and thank God for it, for I doubt our crew of ill and exhausted men could have put up much of a fight against gales of even moderate force. Carruthers assures me that the resumption of near-full rations made possible by our purchases from the whaling vessel we encountered in August made all the difference to the men, but nevertheless I am grateful the crossing was not taxing.

Tomorrow we reach London: home. The men anticipate our arrival with a complacent sort of pleasure, as if they cannot really believe it to be so imminent. I cannot blame them; there is a sense of unreality that permeates us all these days. Can it be that our terrible adventure is at an end? I suppose we must all believe it when at last we see London rise before our eyes. It will not be long now.

I cannot conclude these remarks without noticing the noble spirit and patriotic feeling that has animated the ship's company during our almost super-human exertions, such as it has fallen to the lot of but few to encounter. I know what they have endured, I have witnessed their courage and daring in many eventful scenes; I have seen their manly forms gradually shrink under hunger and cold, and have marked their patience and fortitude when suffering from disease. All this they have borne for the sake of a fellow sailor, for Captain Caulderson, and although we return without a single *Vanguard* survivor and only the saddest tidings of that ship's fate, it cannot be said that our labour has been in vain.

* * * * *

Captain's Log
13 September 1852

I have become as adept as Caulderson himself at writing pretty words and telling sanctioned stories. It does not please me. The truth is that the *Serapis*, under my command, ultimately failed to locate Caulderson and failed to discover the Northwest Passage. I have lost good men, and caused many more to suffer.

I have failed, whatever judgement Sir Francis may pass on my performance. I will not command a ship again.

* * * * *

The Daily Telegraph
Shipping News,Page Nine
15 September 1852

Private ship *Serapis* under Captain David Maxwell has docked in London, returning from a Northern expedition not less than a year later than expected. Details on cargo and expedition aims are scarce, although noted naturalist Embleton Hall is believed to have been aboard and thus the mission may be assumed to have been exploratory and scientific in nature.

* * * * *

Message hand-delivered to ship *Serapis*
London Docks
15 September, 1852

Captain Maxwell,

Welcome home, and heartiest congratulations on your safe return. Please join me immediately at my home for a full report and accounting of your voyage. Bring all ship's logs and rosters, and do expect to be thorough.

I shall expect you early this afternoon.

Most sincerely,
Sir Francis Hall

* * * * *

TELEGRAPHIC MESSAGE: Embleton Hall to Sir Francis Hall (15 September 1852)

FATHER NO STOP HE NEEDS TO REST STOP COME TO THE DOCKS STOP HOTEL IBIS STOP OR WAIT A DAY STOP

* * * * *

TELEGRAPHIC MESSAGE: Sir Francis Hall to Embleton Hall (15 September 1852)

GRATIFIED TO LEARN OF SAFE RETURN STOP YOU SEEM MOST CONCERNED WITH CAPTAIN MAXWELL'S WELLBEING STOP I TRUST YOU HAVE BEEN AS CAREFUL WITH YOUR OWN STOP TOMORROW AFTERNOON THEN STOP COME TOGETHER STOP

* * * * *

15 September 1852

TO: Mrs. Addie Maxwell
23 Little Eastcheap Street
London

Addie,

A brief note, my darling, to tell you I am home; we docked in London this morning. It is inexcusable to send a letter instead of coming myself, I know, but do forgive me if you can. I have never been quite so exhausted in my life. It was all I could do to walk across from the ship to the Ibis. I am well – do not fear – I am well. I simply must rest. Come to me here, quick as you can. If I do not see you here, I shall come home to you on the morrow. I have much to tell you. God! I shall not rest easy until I lay my eyes on you and assure myself of your wellbeing.

With love,
Your husband David
Room 7
Hotel Ibis
London Docks

* * * * *

16 September 1852

Miss Hannah Crawley
54 Oxford Street
London

My dearest Hannah,

I am home. I am home, praise God, at last! And the first thought in my head since I saw London – finally! – appear in the distance, has been to come to you, to look on you, to touch you, to hold you, to have you for my own.

Ah, Hannah. You dear, precious thing. It has been the thought of you that has sustained me these past, terrible months, and my faith in the constancy of your love. But all of our trials are now past! I would endure a dozen – a hundred! – such miseries to spare you pain; I would do all within my power to guard your peace and happiness.

Make your arrangements with your father, if you can; I will wait for you at noon tomorrow at our usual rendezvous spot. If you cannot, write to me here, and guard your letter from *him*. I plan to marry you, Hannah, at the first opportunity. My pay from this expedition will be enough to purchase a little cottage where we can be happy together for the rest of our lives. I shall find work in the docks, for I have had quite enough of life at sea. No circumstance can now keep us apart.

Your loving,
Lew
Room 11
Hotel Ibis
London Docks

* * * * *

Personal Diary
David Maxwell
16 September 1852
11:00

Never before have I kept a diary, but it seems I have grown accustomed aboard ship to recording my thoughts, and now I do not wish to do without it. When I woke this morning after almost 24 hours of sleep, I sent a boy out to fetch me a cheap notebook and some clothing for myself and Hall, for our trunks have not yet been unloaded from the

Serapis. I then ordered up a breakfast: tea and toast, kippers, deviled kidneys, stewed fruits, bread, cheese, ale. The luxuries of this dingy dockland hotel are – almost unimaginable. I look around and cannot quite believe that I am really here.

Strange, too, to be so suddenly separated from the men with whom I have endured the most difficult two years of my life. A few are here in the Ibis with us – Taylor has taken a room down the hall – but many have simply vanished back to the lives they left behind them when first they stepped aboard *Serapis.* One cannot blame them, but it is – strange – to be without them.

I have not heard from Addie. I begin to worry. Surely, had she received my letter, she would have flown to me – or at the very least, sent an immediate reply. I must discharge my last duty as expedition captain and see to my patron this afternoon, but after that – I will find her.

Embleton dealt with the telegrams yesterday, for I was almost delirious with exhaustion and in no fit state to do anything but collapse. But this morning, he has shown me. Sir Francis requires all of the expedition logs and a full accounting of the journey. Of course, I knew he should, and yet – so much of what went on feels private. I feel that it is not for him, nor for anyone who was not there.

I would sooner burn my Captain's Log than turn it over to anyone, let alone Embleton's own father. God! I shall bring the Ship's Log, and hope that it will suffice. Nay – it *will* suffice, and that is the end of it.

How strange it is to be back in London. How loud! The noise outside my window just now is –

I am quite dizzy with it.

Embleton tells me we may put Sir Francis off for as long as we wish; he is most concerned for my health. I desire to remain within his good graces, however, for I have it in mind that each surviving crew member shall receive a substantial additional financial benefit on top of his contracted salary to account for the damage done to his health and the hardship each man has endured.

It is strange, not to sleep with him. We cannot risk discovery – not here, where consequences would be so dire. It is dreadfully cold and I shiver constantly when he is not near, as if the Arctic ice had taken up residence under my very skin, so that I can never shed it but shall always feel myself within its icy, intractable grip. He is worried, I think, about what will happen when Addie comes – although he knows how well I love him. I do not know how to explain that he need not worry. I love my wife; and still, he is my heart.

* * * * *

TELEGRAPHIC MESSAGE: Abiah Higginbotham to David Maxwell (16 September 1852)

HAVE JUST HEARD OF YOUR SAFE RETURN STOP THANK GOD STOP APOLOGIES FOR DELAY STOP ADDIE IS ABROAD STOP THE HOUSE IN EASTCHEAP ST IS SOLD STOP I FOLLOW THIS MESSAGE BY TRAIN AND WILL EXPLAIN ALL

* * * * *

Naturalist's Log
Final entry
16 September 1852

In lieu of my complete expedition logs, which are filled with notes of a private nature and trifling observations that will interest none but myself, I offer this summary of my scientific work and findings from the duration of the *Serapis's* expedition. In the coming year, I shall publish several manuscripts detailing the specifics of my findings and outlining new theories based upon these.

The following pages comprise lists of the most significant fauna and flora met with in the polar sea during the voyage, and of which specimens were obtained. Drawings and anatomical details are in the appended files, with specimens preserved in the naturalist's personal collection. Plant specimens are included with place markers and drawings.

The preparations of mammalia and pisces include the skins, skeletons, and such of the viscera as I consider worthy of preservation. Insecta and invertebrata are preserved separately. A few specimens of the crustaceous and acephalous animals I have reserved for more accurate examination than it lay in my power to bestow on them aboard ship.

I may remark, that in the Western Islands (Baring and Melville), where the soil is arenaceous, animal life is more abundant than elsewhere; this gradually decreases to the eastward, where the limestone formation generally prevails. But the greater number of Bears, Seals, Walruses, and Sea-fowl met with – although these are more difficult to procure than Musk-Oxen or Reindeer – by their great size afford sufficient compensation; the carbonaceous element of the food (fat), the great supporter of respiration and life, being so largely supplied.

In closing, I may say that although the difficulties of an Arctic voyage are considerable and the scientist may suffer great privations and hardships, I have never had a more educative experience, and I am all gratitude to Captain Maxwell and his excellent men for extending me the privilege of their forbearance.

✲ ✲ ✲ ✲ ✲

Personal Diary
David Maxwell
22 September 1852

Still very tired; my body feels leaden and I sleep away many hours of each day. Carruthers has come to see me every day since we docked, as he has kindly done with all the crew, and tells me it is no more than I should expect. He prescribes only rest and food in large quantity and variety, to which I am pleased to submit. Indeed, I could hardly do otherwise, for Embleton all but guards my door, and brings me meals at regular intervals. He looks tired himself, but he insists that he slept adequately during our crossing, which is certainly the case. He will not sleep with me now even in the daylight hours for fear of discovery. I suppose he is prudent. I only wish I could lie with him; it is the only time I feel at all warm.

I have just two events of note to report.

The first: We've left the Ibis just once since our arrival, to report to Sir Francis Hall at his very impressive home on 17 September. I was hesitant to bring Embleton, knowing something of their relations, but after all – it is not for me to stand between them.

Our interview was surprisingly brief, although a silent war seemed to wage between the Halls, *père et fils*, the entire time. I felt entirely bewildered and not yet well enough, or quick enough, to follow. I handed over the Ship's Log, as well as Embleton's summation of his own log, and a lengthy statement from Carruthers, and explained that my personal log would hold no interest to him. Embleton glared quite forcibly, then, and Sir Francis only blinked and nodded, paging through the log.

"Caulderson is dead, obviously?" he asked. His voice was mild, but his expression was grim.

I nodded. "He is, God rest his soul, and all his men. We discovered the site of the *Vanguard's* sinking – almost exactly where you suspected it would be, sir – and several camps made by the last surviving crewmen.

They are all dead of cold and hunger and sickness. Full details are related in the ship's log." Caulderson's own last logs – the most damning evidence against him – will be kept forever locked in my strongbox, with Embleton and I the only men in the world to know the complete story. His ring is locked up, too; it is not mine to wear.

"And the Passage?"

"Remains untraversed and unclaimed."

Sir Francis drew a deep breath. "It is not the outcome I had hoped for."

I said nothing. I could not imagine his motives for involving himself in the case in the first place. I shivered suddenly, and moved nearer to the great fire burning on the hearth. Embleton moved to stand beside me, and I felt the ghost of a touch to my back; it was as warming as the fire itself.

Sir Francis was at the window, staring out unseeingly.

After a time, Embleton sighed. "We are exhausted, father. Ask your questions, and allow us to depart."

Sir Francis looked up sharply at Embleton, then, raising an eyebrow. To my astonishment, Embleton flushed.

"Very well," he said. "I shall read the ship's log thoroughly, and will have many questions afterwards – but that can wait. Tell me, though, did Caulderson himself leave no logs?"

I shrugged. "We discovered some early logs and letters – they are appended to the *Serapis's* log. There is nothing of great import."

Sir Francis's eyes narrowed, but he nodded. "Go and rest," he said. "We shall meet again when you have recovered your strength, and when I have had an opportunity to read through the logs."

I thanked him, and turned to exit the room, but Embleton gripped my arm and held me fast. "There is one last matter to which we must attend," he said, and went on to most eloquently and effectively argue for the payment of a large gratuity to each surviving member of our crew. His father's eyebrows rose precipitously, and had nearly disappeared into his hair by the time Embleton had stated his case.

"Please, father," he concluded. "These men saved my life more than once. There is no amount of money that can truly compensate them for the horrors they have endured these past years, but if we can make their lives a little easier now, a little more comfortable – we owe it to them to do so."

Sir Francis smiled coolly. "I should be pleased to make the *Serapis* men's lives more comfortable, as you say – upon one condition, Em. No more drugging. Do not return to your previous habits. I will not have it!"

"Nor will I," I added, quite forgetting myself. I can only blame my exhaustion for such freedom of speech, but Sir Francis merely looked hard at Embleton.

"I have no such plans," Embleton said, wincing.

"Well then," the other returned smoothly. "Arrangements have already been made."

I have no doubt that Sir Francis will interrogate me most thoroughly about the log at some future time, but for now I am too exhausted to worry overmuch. Embleton tucked me into a cab and we returned at once to the Ibis where I fell at once into a deep sleep.

The only other event of note upon which I must report is a brief visit from Miss Abiah Higginbotham, my wife's very dear friend and confidante. Miss Higginbotham brought news of Addie that filled me with sorrow. She had a difficult time of it while I was away, and suffered many disappointments. I cannot regret my expedition, but greatly do I regret leaving her to face her demons alone. It was necessary, but it was not right. I will write to her, for she shall always be my wife, and I shall always love her with a husband's love. Perhaps one day she will return to

England and I shall look upon her face once more. But for now: I am accustomed to loving an absence.

⁂ ⁂ ⁂ ⁂ ⁂

19 September 1852

TO: Landlord
#37 Old Burlington Street
London W1

Dear Sir,

Having recently returned to London from voyages abroad, I find myself in need of a suite of rooms to accommodate myself and an associate. We are professional gentlemen of most respectable habits, I a naturalist of some repute, and he a former ship's captain.

We discovered your advertisement in an old edition of the *Times* left behind in our current, temporary lodgings, and wondered if your rooms are still available. The location would suit us admirably. Two bedrooms and a sitting room are required, with minimal attendance.

I shall call upon you tomorrow afternoon If this does not suit, please reply by return post.

Sincerely,
Mr. E. Hall

⁂ ⁂ ⁂ ⁂ ⁂

Disbursed to each surviving crew member of the *Serapis*, and to the families of the men who died in service, with all compliments and thanks, from Sir Francis Hall: the sum of £80 in addition to contracted wages.

⁂ ⁂ ⁂ ⁂ ⁂

21 September 1852

TO: Mrs. Addie Maxwell
Poste Restante Centrale
Paris

My dearest Addie,

I trust this letter will reach you. I write only to tell you that I am back in London, that I have seen Miss Higginbotham, and that I love and miss you.

Caulderson is dead. He died in terrible circumstances many months before we reached him. I do not know what to say about our expedition or its discoveries. It is too much for words, and I do not yet know how to speak of it. But – there is someone I should very much like you to meet one day.

Addie, I do not understand all that Miss Higginbotham told me, but I know enough to see that you have been dreadfully hurt these past years. I am so sorry. You are one of the few souls in the world to ever truly have known me, and I thank you for it. I hope you find a way back to happiness, and would do anything to help you if I could. I remain

Your loving husband,
David Maxwell

PS. Please write back, if you see fit. I shall send you an address the instant I find somewhere more permanent to live. Since I cannot now see you, I would see letters formed by your hand.

* * * * *

TELEGRAPHIC MESSAGE: Sir Francis Hall to Embleton Hall (20 September 1852)

UNSATISFACTORY STOP MOST UNSATISFACTORY STOP THE INFORMATION CONTAINED IN THE SHIPS LOG IS NOT

SUFFICIENT STOP MAXWELL MUST HAND OVER HIS OWN LOG AND YOU MUST BOTH TELL THE COMPLETE STORY OF YOUR VOYAGE STOP IT WILL NOT STAND STOP

* * * * *

TELEGRAPHIC MESSAGE: Embleton Hall to Sir Francis Hall (20 September 1852)

SOME THINGS ARE NOT FOR YOU STOP

* * * * *

23 September 1852

TO: Mr. Lew Taylor
Hotel Ibis
London Docks

Dear Lew,

Please excuse my delay in replying to your letter: it took several days to reach me as I am no longer living in Oxford Street. I was wretched to miss the rendezvous you suggested – but it is for the best. I have been thrown into such confusion that I hardly know where to leave myself. I thank God for your safe return, Lew. I thank God for it! I despaired of it, may God forgive me.

Thank God that you are home, safe and well.

So much has changed! So much. *I* have changed, Lew. I cannot meet you. I cannot meet you ever again, and if I see you on the street I must pass by without stopping. I am not your Hannah anymore, and never can be again. I am Mrs. Brown. I am not the girl you knew; that girl is dead, and if you ever loved her, you must mourn her now and forget.

I am sorry. Forgive me. Please do not write again.

Mrs. Brown
Secretary, Women's Suffrage Committee
#9 Harley Street
London W1

* * * * *

Personal Diary
David Maxwell
23 September 1852

At 08:00 this morning, a carriage stopped outside the Ibis and two rather large and burly gentlemen pulled us from our breakfast. We were quite forcibly hustled into the carriage without a word; I would have resisted, but Embleton's look of utter disdain and his rolling eyes told me all I needed to know about who was behind the interruption.

"I've been ignoring his telegrams," he muttered to me. "But even for father, this is excessive."

I hid a smile behind my hand. The Halls are more alike than either would care to admit.

Our apparent captors escorted us to Sir Francis's private study, where the man himself sat like Solomon behind his imposing oak desk.

"Really, father," Embleton protested. There was a childish tinge to his voice that I'd not heard before. "This was hardly necessary. Captain Maxwell was in the middle of his breakfast!"

"Saunders will bring tea," he snapped. "You have both behaved most irresponsibly! This so-called log is a disgrace!"

I felt the colour slowly blanch from my face, but Embleton, seated beside me, slumped casually back into his chair as if he had not the least concern.

All I knew – the only thing that mattered to me in that moment – was that William Caulderson's reputation be preserved, and that no taint of scandal or any disreputable conduct ever mar his memory. I had failed to rescue him, but I should not fail in this.

"And what, pray, is the problem?" Embleton asked carelessly.

"Details, Embleton!" Sir Francis bellowed, and began to lecture us both on exactly the type of details he wished for. "Why do you imagine I financed this endeavour?" he at last demanded. "For *science*? Please. This is business, and I require some return on my investment. I need facts! I must understand why Caulderson failed, so that I can mount another campaign and be the first to gain the Passage. The profit would be incalculable! This –" he gestured scoffingly to the ship's log that lay on his desk – "this vague dribble tells me only that you are obscuring the vital facts of the case."

I shook my head. "I have faithfully reported the truth: Caulderson and his men are dead, and the *Vanguard* destroyed. There's nothing else you need know."

Sir Francis leaned over his desk, looking at me intently. "If you care so little for business, think of your country. The race to discover the Northwest Passage is nothing less than a battle for the supremacy of the empire."

Embleton stirred. "Then it is a battle we must lose, and we are fools to base the ostensible supremacy of our empire on such an uncertain foundation."

"Don't be naive. We are but foot soldiers in the relentless campaign of Progress. If we do not find the passage, someone else will – and how should that serve us? Caulderson has come closer than anyone else, and we must – we *must* – know the details of his failure."

And then, before my eyes, I saw the scene shift, and instead of Sir Francis's fine study with its tall windows, its good leather armchairs and shelves upon shelves of beautiful books, I felt myself transported once more to the vast fields of ice and snow from which I had so recently returned, and it seemed for a moment that I was flying, soaring above, and I saw bright pools of crimson in the snow, and I saw Esquimeaux bleeding and dying horribly, and the *Vanguard*, collapsing under the ice with men staring up from the depths of the icy sea with eyes like dead things, and there, too, was Caulderson, and he was lying naked in the snow, and he was dying. They were all dying together.

I was shaking my head already when I came back to myself with a convulsive shudder.

Beside me, Embleton spoke. "This is not a battle, father, and what you call the march of progress may advance in many ways. It is foolish – dangerous and foolish – to conceive of it as a war. It is only a war if we *make* it one, and if this is your project I, for one, will not aid it."

Sir Francis sat back in his chair. His face had flushed a little during this speech, but he said nothing in reply.

In the uncomfortable lull, Saunders knocked discreetly and came in with a tea tray. I could barely conceive of it: taking tea and politely conversing after – after everything. Perhaps I am not yet sufficiently recovered; I began to shake, and by the time Saunders was pouring out my teeth were rattling in my head. I could not have held a teacup steady to save my life. I began to feel quite dizzy. Embleton looked at me in some alarm.

"Captain Maxwell is not yet well," he said, rising. "He must rest. Father, we may return to this conversation at a later date – although I think you'll find us both intractable on this point." He took my arm and raised me up, drawing me from the room.

Hoarsely, I wished Sir Francis a polite good morning, and departed without looking back. Embleton was quite wrong: I shall not revisit that conversation ever again.

* * * * *

TELEGRAPHIC MESSAGE from Sir Francis Hall to Vice Admiral Joseph Baring (23 September 1852)

IN STRICT CONFIDENCE

NO FURTHER INFORMATION OBTAINED STOP THE PASSAGE REMAINS UNDISCOVERED AND UNCLAIMED STOP SUGGEST RUNNING NEXT ATTEMPT THROUGH NAVY STOP

* * * * *

Personal Diary
David Maxwell
3 October 1852

My God. Embleton – dear, marvellous, brilliant Embleton – has found us a home! A home that we can make together, where we can shut the door to the world and fall together in perfect safety and security. We can even share a bed. *Our* bed. *Our* home. How very well it sounds.

We have two bedrooms – the second for propriety – and a large and comfortable private sitting room. The fire is always lit. We are always dry and warm.

We moved in on the first of the month: easy enough, for we both have several cases and a trunk from the ship, and that is all. The landlord, a Mr. Brentwood by name, has provided all the necessary furnishings with a most severe and disinterested demeanor; his attendance is satisfactorily nominal. Surprising to me, Em seems quite amused by him.

To our mutual shock, Sir Francis has sent over a crate of extremely specialized laboratory equipment for Embleton's use, and a veritable library of what I believe must be every book published in England in the last two years for my "edification and amusement." He is utterly inscrutable, but I do believe him to be sincere in his wish for Embleton's health and happiness.

We've had unexpected visitor, as well: Lew Taylor stepped in, looking worse, almost, than he did when we first arrived in London. He begged my assistance in finding a cheap berth to the Cape Colony, where he has some distant relations. It transpires that he's been sorely disappointed by his young lady, and seeks to begin his life anew on other shores. I grieve to lose such a man – such a friend – but shall do my best for him. We owe him our lives several times over; the very least we can do is see him settled in his own.

I have been thinking of what to do with myself, now that our expedition is ended. I have not yet fully recovered, nor has Embleton, but Carruthers assures me that we shall both be right as rain within the next several months. Money is apparently not a consideration for the Hall family, and Embleton assures me that I need not work if I do not wish to, but I remember how very miserable I used to be – haunting the docks and walking endlessly, aimlessly... I would not risk a return to such a life. Embleton has his work to occupy his time, and I must have something of my own. I think sometimes of writing the story of our Arctic adventure, as so many expedition commanders have done before me, but I cannot quite see how the thing could be done both safely and truthfully. Embleton snorts and insults my "lazy faculty of creation" when I speak of it; he believes it would simply require careful phrasing and transposition of facts. I wonder...

Speaking of Embleton, he has abandoned his strange fascination with viscera in favour of a new intellectual obsession with ravens, about which he has decided to write a monograph. He will tell me nothing of the contents, but slaves over it for hours each day, darting about on occasion to visit various libraries and laboratories around the city. The book is apparently based upon his observations in the Arctic, but still requires extensive research. He claims that it will make his name, and I have learned not to doubt him.

He is happy – and he is extraordinary, my Embleton. If the remainder of my life is dedicated to nothing more than witnessing his, I will consider it a life well-lived.

* * * * *

Manuscript in preparation (November 1852)
The Arctic Raven: Some Thoughts and Observations Upon the Corvus corax with Particular Attention Paid to Social and Mating Behaviours
By Embleton Hall

The common raven (*Corvus corax*), also known as the northern raven, is a large all-black passerine bird. Found across the Northern Hemisphere, it is the most widely distributed of all corvids. There are at least eight subspecies with little variation in appearance, although recent research has demonstrated significant genetic differences among populations from various regions. It is one of the two largest corvids, alongside the thick-billed raven, and is possibly the heaviest passerine bird; at maturity, the common raven averages 25 inches in length and 2.6 pounds in mass. Common ravens can live up to 21 years in the wild, a lifespan exceeded among passerines by only a few Australasian species such as the satin bowerbird and perhaps the lyrebirds. Young birds may travel in flocks but later mate for life, with each mated pair defending a territory.

The associations into which feeding birds enter are many and varied. The simplest are bands of birds brought together by gregariousness; one of the most complex has elements that have earned for it the term "symbiosis." And yet the great diversity is not without order. Surveying the many types of flocking or associations one sees that they can be arranged into series, from simple to complex. Not only that, but the series inter-relate, until rather than a chain or a "tree" we have a whole network or fabric, with analogies reaching out in many directions.

Though advanced, complicated behaviors likely arose out of simple behaviors; many of the behavior patterns we see probably arose independently, from the basic similarity of birds, the recurrence of similar situations, and the acuity of many birds in profiting by small advantages in their environment.

Using collected specimens and observational data to sort out blood relationships, it is possible to see how birds have met the problems of their environments, and how their innate tendencies and their physical equipment have resulted in varying behavior patterns under various conditions, or similar patterns under similar conditions, irrespective of relationships.

Such an arrangement based on likenesses is of value in showing how behavior could have originated. Though the more complex behavior cited below did not arise out of the simpler behavior described, it probably did arise from similar simple behavior. A "pseudo-phyletic" series is a term that could be employed for the arrangements used below, and seems more self-explanatory than the "biological series" of Dr. Boker, among others. These arrangements give us a framework and a background against which to view examples of behavior.

* * * * *

Manuscript in preparation (December 1852)
The Arctic Adventures of the Ship Serapis
By David Maxwell, Captain

Preface

In this story are contained many stories, and perhaps it appears contradictory to say that all of them are true – and yet, this is the case. My friend Mr. Embleton Hall would say that I must seek truth above all things, using facts to support the telling; I cannot do so, however, without acknowledging the many truths that twine together, pulling each other this way and that, growing stronger as they grow into each other.

This is a story about William Caulderson. No. No – it is a story about a brave voyage of glorious discovery in lands where the stories we tell dissolve into nonsense and cease to mean anything at all; lands where we are forced to write new ones. Nay – it is about a foolhardy voyage into a world made of ice, brittle and groaning under the weight of too many stories. It is a story about Embleton Hall. It is an adventure. It is a love story. It is a tragedy. It is a war story. It is a story of friendship. It is an elegy. It is a travelogue. It is an end. It is a beginning.

The only thing I know about this story is that I must write it; I can do nothing else. Perhaps you will see aspects of your own story reflected back to you in these pages – perhaps, indeed, every story belongs, in some way, to every man.

✲ ✲ ✲ ✲ ✲

Uukkarnit, the annatko from Igluligaarjuk, speaks the story every year as the long night begins:

My mother, and her father, and her father's mother, and many before them, spoke of the Tuniit, the people who inhabited the land before the Inuit came. They were a different stock of people: taller and stronger, with the muscularity of polar bears. A Tuniit man could lift a 1,000 pound seal on his back, or drag a whole walrus. They built stone longhouses that still stand today: you can see them at Mallikjuag and Nunguvik. They might stand forever. Some say the Tuniit slept with their legs in the air to drain the blood from their feet and make them lighter. Some say they could outrun a caribou.

But also, they were shy. They were silent. They were easily put to flight, and it was seldom heard that they killed others. The Inuit took over the best hunting camps and displaced the Tuniit, who would not fight them. Soon enough, these strange people disappeared from the land. They died or they moved on. No one knows how they went.

Aya aya aya
I am not the Tuniit
I will not disappear from the land.
Aya aya aya

Aya aya aya
We are not the Tuniit
We will not disappear from the land.
Aya aya aya

Aya aya aya
We will not disappear from this land.
Aya aya aya
Aya aya aya
Aya aya aya

Epilogue:
2014

William Caulderson's long-lost HMS Vanguard believed found
By Maurice LaMotte, CBC News
Posted: July 12, 2014 10:46 AM CT

Prime Minster Stephen Harper today announced the history-making discovery of the HMS *Vanguard*, British explorer William Caulderson's ship famously lost in a doomed 1845 expedition to discover the Northwest Passage.

In a press room hastily decorated with a large map of the country, the phrase "A STRONG CANADA" repeated across it in both official languages, Harper looked uncharacteristically elated. "This is truly a historic moment for Canada," he said, announcing the successful culmination of six years of searching in the Arctic and the investment of millions of dollars of public money.

"Caulderson's ship is an important part of Canadian history, given that his expedition, which took place nearly 200 years ago, laid the foundations of Canada's Arctic sovereignty," Harper said. "This discovery confirms, without shadow of doubt, Canada's claim to our Arctic lands."

A video shared with CBC News and produced by the Arctic Research Foundation appears to show images of the submerged HMS *Vanguard*. "Divers spotted wine bottles, tables, and empty shelving. They saw a desk with open drawers, a canon, ceramic plates… It's quite extraordinary," ARF spokesman Larysa Janiv said by email.

Academic and amateur historians are similarly excited. The discovery "has the potential to alter forever our understanding of the Caulderson Expedition's disastrous end," says Peter Flemming, a historian with the University College of the North.

One mystery still remains: the location of Caulderson's grave. Whether he went down with his ship, or whether he and his men escaped the sinking and died on the ice, no one has yet discovered. The man who came closest, Captain David Maxwell of the somewhat mysterious 1850 *Serapis* expedition, wrote and published an account of his findings that Flemming calls "maddeningly, almost deliberately vague."

The discovery of the *Vanguard* was made possible only with the assistance of Inuit oral history, adds Nunavut Arctic College historian Henry Okpik, who helped researchers pinpoint the location of the wreck after repeatedly encountering oral histories suggesting the ship was crushed in ice off of King William Island.

Parks Canada has agreed to seek permission from Nunavut's director of heritage before divers remove *Vanguard* artifacts. "The discovery of HMS *Vanguard* is important for Canada, reflecting the ongoing and valuable role of Inuit traditional knowledge in the search and making a significant contribution to completing the Caulderson story," a Parks Canada spokesperson said.

"Every time there's a finding, it's kind of a sad feeling," Okpik added. "It's the beginning of scientific study of the artifact, but it's the death of the living story."

Author's Note and Acknowledgements

This is a work of fiction, but the expeditions described here are loosely based on the Franklin Expedition and the subsequent recovery missions that followed its disappearance in 1845. There are many excellent sources on the Franklin expedition. My primary historical source, from which I sometimes adapted material, was *A Personal Narrative of the Discovery of the Northwest Passage* by Alex Armstrong (1857). A secondary source, particularly for the overland expedition, was *Narrative of a Second Voyage in Search of a North-west Passage* by James Clark Ross (1835)

I also looked at first-person accounts by the women left behind, for example, those collected in "As affecting the fate of my absent husband": Selected Letters of Lady Franklin Concerning the Search for the Lost Franklin Expedition, 1848-1860, edited by Erika Behrisch Elce (2009). Addie's views on suffrage are modeled on Harriet Taylor's article "Enfranchisement of Women," from the Westminster and Foreign Quarterly Review for July 1851. The failed suffrage petition is a real historical event, and the pamphlets Addie shares with Hannah are real publications.

Colonialism is an important theme here. This is an epistolary novel; it consists of letters and other "found" documents. Inuit culture was oral. History and information were passed from person to person, community to community, and generation to generation in the form of stories and songs, which I have included here as Inuit epistolary voices. Much of what I've included is adapted from verbatim oral histories recorded in *Unraveling the Franklin Mystery: Inuit Testimony* by David C. Woodman (1991), and *Encounters on the Passage: Inuit Meet the Explorers* by Dorothy Harley Eber (2008). Historical tellings of Inuit myths are from Knud Rasmussen's *Eskimo Folk Tales* (1921).

I use historically-appropriate terminology throughout. The Inuit refer to themselves as such, and the Europeans call them "Esquimeaux" – a derogatory term. The Inuit call the Europeans "qallunaat," sometimes anglicized in European texts as "kabloona." Gerald Prince's chapter "On a Postcolonial Narratology" in *A Companion to Narrative Theory* was extremely helpful to me in thinking through the inherent colonialism of exploration literature.

As a story about stories, *A Land so Wild* makes reference to many works of literature. These include poems by John Donne and William Wordsworth, the novels *David Copperfield* by Charles Dickens and *Clarissa* by Samuel Richardson, and the play *The Frozen Deep* by Wilkie Collins and Charles Dickens. Some of Embleton Hall's observations about ravens were inspired by *The Social Feeding Behaviour of Birds* by Austin L. Rand (1954).

Thank you to the early readers of this work for their support and valuable feedback: Beatriz Contreras, Jaime Lilley, Karen Schwartz, Peter Warkentin, Val Warkentin, Erika Wiebe, and the readers at Archive Of Our Own. Thanks to Elise Mitchell and Penny Armstrong for preliminary editing and advice, and to R.K. Taylor for her terrifically insightful, generous, and nuanced editing. Sincere thanks as well to Lee Douglass and Colleen Veillon at Carnation Books.

And of course, thanks and love to my boys.

Translations from Chapter Nine:

Greek translation: What cannot be said is wept (Sappho).

Italian translation: What is the process called? Siamo il ghiaccio [we are the ice]. Crystals dissolving and resolidifying, un cicolo terrible, sublime [a terrible and sublime cycle]. He is my solvent and I his. Solvation, that is the name. No, salvazione. Il liquido diviene cristallo [salvation. Liquid becomes crystal], volume becomes mass, becomes an anchor. Mi ancoro in lui e lui in me [I anchor myself in him and he in me].

German translation: If we are to die here, we will at least have had this

About Carnation Books

Carnation Books is a fandom-powered publisher of the best in inclusive fiction. Founded in 2016, Carnation Books is at the forefront of new author discovery. Visit carnationbooks.com to learn more, and to sign up for our story-filled newsletter!

Made in the USA
Lexington, KY
05 December 2018